C000176739

50 THINGS TO COLOUR

Apple Press, a division of Quarto Publishing Group UK
74-77 White Lion Street
London N1 9PF UK
www.apple-press.com

Cover design by Shelley Baugh.

ISBN 978-1-84543-611-7

Manufactured in China.

10 9 8 7 6 5 4 3 2

50 THINGS TO COLOUR

50 Creative Projects to Unleash Your Colouring Skills

Susan Hogan Tice

APPLE

Table of Contents

Tools and Materials

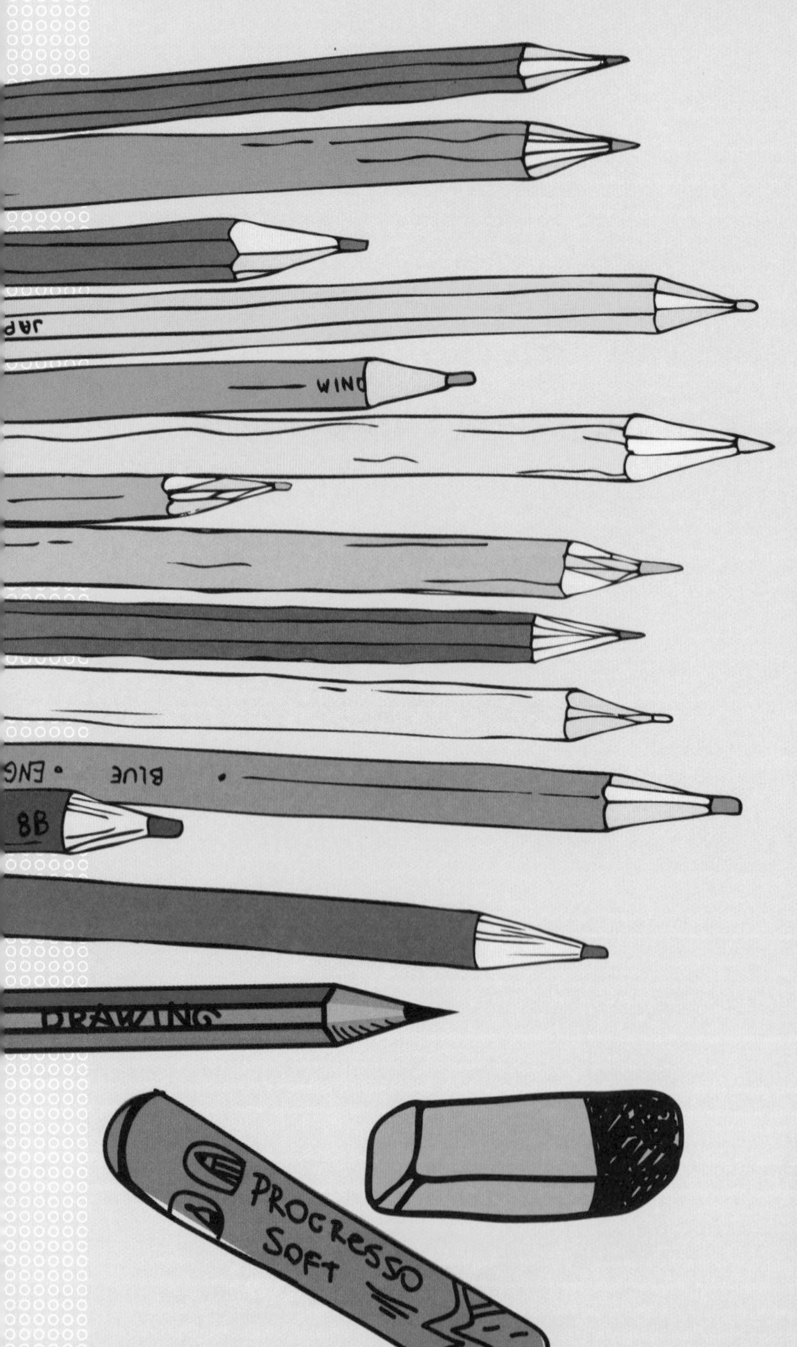

Coloured Pencils
I recommend a starter set that contains the following colours, or their nearest equivalents: grey, mineral orange, espresso, crimson lake, indigo blue, magenta, true blue, dark green, light green, goldenrod, orange, poppy red, violet and black. Many art and craft shops sell pencils individually, making it easy to mix and match your pencils and add to your colour palette as needed.

Erasers
Use a rubber eraser to erase light applications of colour when using coloured pencils. You may also take a kneadable eraser and dab at the area to pick up the pigment. Wall mounting putty is very useful when used the same way. For stubborn areas, use a battery-powered eraser.

Sharpener
Use a hand-held sharpener to give your coloured pencils sharp tips. A fine point can be used to create extremely thin lines and colour in small details. You can also use the side of a sharp tip to produce thick strokes that are perfect for quickly colouring in large areas.

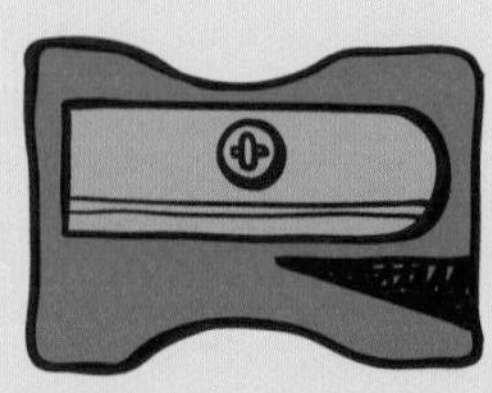

Paints and Paintbrushes

While you may not want to paint directly in the book, feel free to transfer these images to paper or canvas and get your acrylics, watercolours or oils out. I recommend starting with the following colours (or their nearest alternatives): burnt sienna, crimson red, ivory black, lemon yellow, permanent green, ultramarine blue and yellow oche. You may also want to pick up Chinese white for lighter tints. Use a flat brush to cover large areas and apply washes, and a round brush with a tapered point for a variety of paint strokes and fine details.

Markers

Whether permanent or magic, markers are a colouring must-have. The saturated hues of markers are bright and vibrant, just like the artist wielding them – you! Markers come in every colour imaginable and are readily available at all art and craft shops.

Crayons and Pastels

Instantly feel like a kid again opening an eight-pack, or go more advanced with a box of 64 or more. If crayons feel too childish to you, make them classy by going for pastels. Pastels come in a variety of types, mainly soft, hard and oil, and can be used to create dazzling effects involving layered and mixed colours.

Warming Up

Just as you warm up before working out at the gym, you should relax your hand and get comfortable holding the utensils – be they crayons, markers or, in this case, coloured pencils – before exercising your creativity. I usually warm up by drawing random squiggles and lines. Familiarise yourself with the different types of line your pencils can create and experiment with every kind of stroke you can think of, using a sharp point and a blunt point. Practise the strokes below and on the next page to help you loosen up.

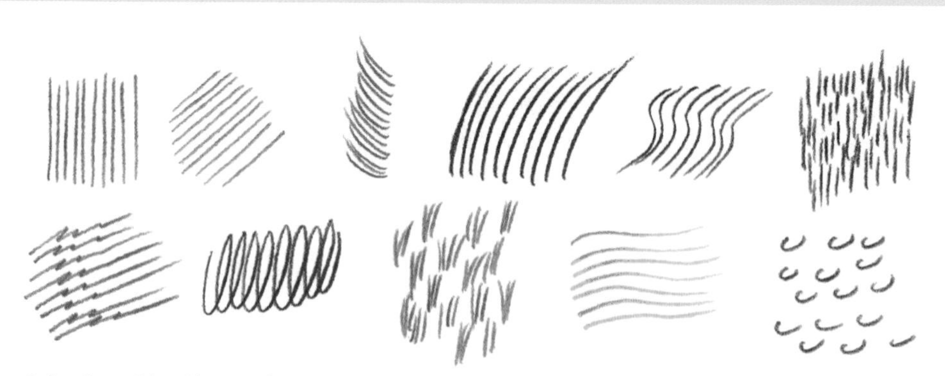

Colouring with a Sharp Point

Firstly, draw a series of parallel lines. Try them vertically, then angle them. Make some of them curved, trying both short and long strokes. Then try some wavy lines at an angle and some with short, vertical strokes. Try making a spiral and then grouping short, curved lines together. Then practice varying the weight of the line as you draw.

Colouring with a Blunt Point

Now try the same lines with a blunt point. Even if you use the same hand positions and strokes, the results will be different when you switch pencils. In the example above, you can see that the blunt pencil produced different effects. You can create a blunt point by rubbing the tip of the pencil on a sandpaper block or on a rough piece of paper.

Starting Simply
First experiment with vertical, horizontal and curved strokes. Keep the strokes close together and begin with heavy pressure. Then lighten the pressure with each stroke.

Varying the Pressure
Randomly cover the area with tone, varying the pressure at different points. Continue to keep your strokes loose.

Using Smaller Strokes
Make small circles for the first example. This looks like leathery animal skin. For the second example (at far right), use short, alternating strokes of heavy and light pressure to create a pattern that is similar to stone or brick.

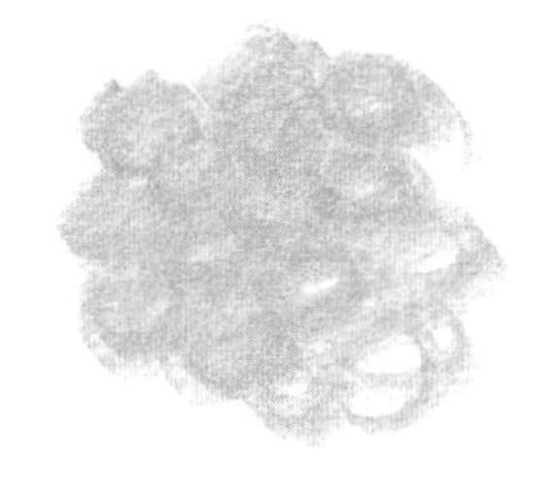

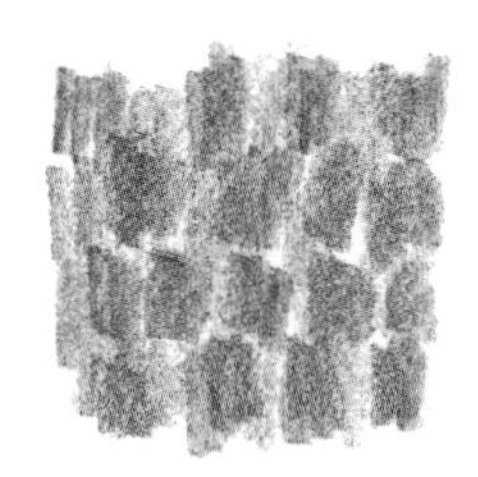

Loosening Up
Use long vertical strokes, varying the pressure for each stroke until you start to see long grass (at near right). Then use somewhat looser movements that could be used for water (at far right). First create short spiral movements with your arm (above). Then use a wavy movement, varying the pressure (below).

Finding Your Style

After a while, you'll notice that your colourings will all take on a consistent look and feel. Don't worry — it's just your own unique style coming through. To jumpstart this process, try experimenting with the different types of linework shown below.

Using Criss-Crossed Strokes
If you like a good deal of fine detail in your work, you'll find that crosshatching allows you a lot of control. You can adjust the depth of your shading by changing the distance between your strokes.

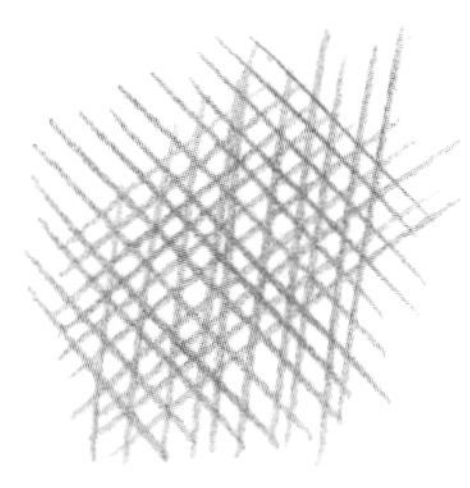

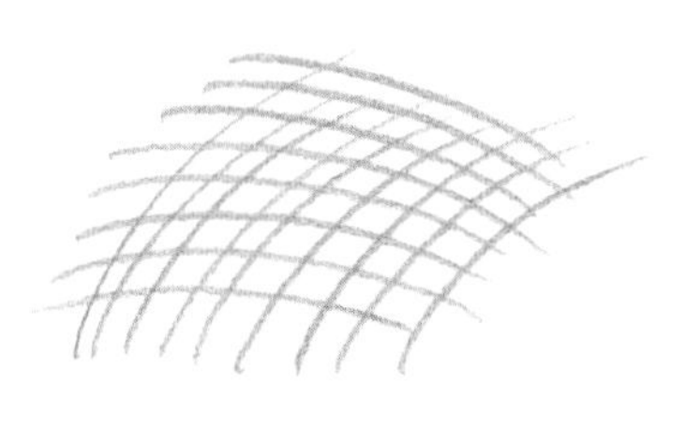

Sketching Circular Scribbles
If you work with round, loose strokes like these, you are probably very experimental with your art. These looping lines suggest a free-form style that is more concerned with evoking a mood than with capturing precise details.

Making Small Dots
This technique is called 'stippling' – many small dots are used to create a larger picture. Make the points different sizes to create various depths and shading effects. Stippling takes a great deal of precision and practice.

Simulating Brushstrokes
You can create the illusion of brushstrokes by using short, sweeping lines. This captures the feeling of painting but allows you the same control you would get from crosshatching. These strokes are ideal for a more stylistic approach.

Colour Values

Value is the term used to describe the relative lightness or darkness of a colour (or of black). By adding a range of values to your subjects, you create the illusion of depth and form. Value defines form, not colour, so if you choose the appropriate values, the colour isn't important – you can draw purple trees or blue dogs and still captivate your viewers.

Creating Form with Value In this example, you can see that the grey objects seem just as three-dimensional as the coloured objects. This shows that value is more important than colour when it comes to creating convincing, lifelike subjects. It's a good idea to practise this exercise before you begin the projects so you can get a handle on applying values. First view the basic shape. Then, starting on the shadowed side, begin building up value, leaving the paper white in the areas where the light hits the object directly. Continue adding values to create the form of the object. Squint your eyes to blur the details so you can focus on the value changes. Add the darkest values last. As the object gets further away from the light, the values become darker, so place the darkest values on the side directly opposite the light.

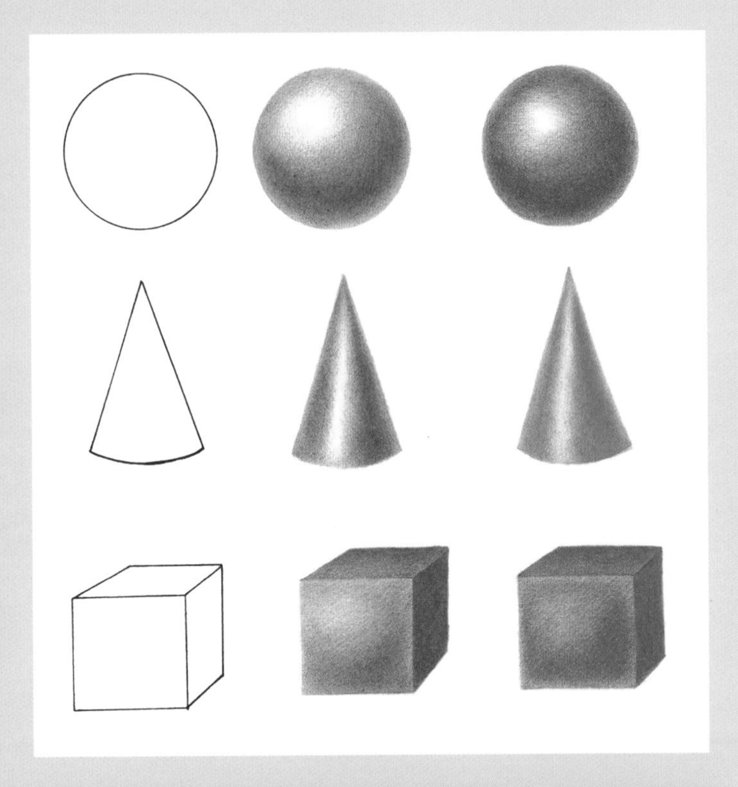

Value Scale Another helpful tool for understanding value is a value scale showing the progression from white (the lightest value) to black (the darkest value). Most coloured pencil brands offer a variety of greys, which are distinguished by naming them either 'warm' or 'cool' and then adding a percentage to indicate the concentration of colour, such as 'cool grey 20%'. (Lower percentages are lighter.) All different colours come in different values, too.

Light and Shadow

Shading gives depth and form to your colouring because it creates contrasts in *value* (the relative lightness or darkness of black or a colour). In pencil drawing, values range from white (the lightest value) through different shades of grey to black (the darkest value; see the value scale below). To make a two-dimensional object appear three-dimensional, pay attention to the values of the highlights and shadows. Imagine the egg below with no shading, only an outline. The egg would just be an oval. But by adding variations of value with light and shadow, the egg appears to have form. When shading a subject, you must always consider the light source, as this is what determines where your highlights and shadows will be. Keep in mind that shadows get darker as they get further from the light source.

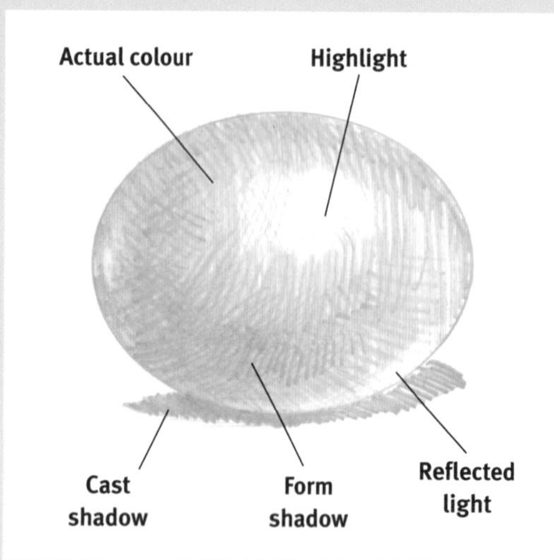

Identifying Values
The *highlight* is the lightest value and is where the light source directly strikes the object. The grey area between the highlight and the shadow is the actual colour of the egg, without any highlights or shadows. The *cast shadow* is the shadow that the egg casts onto the ground. The *form shadow* is the shadow that is on the object itself. *Reflected light* bounces up onto the object from the ground surface. (Most people don't notice that one!)

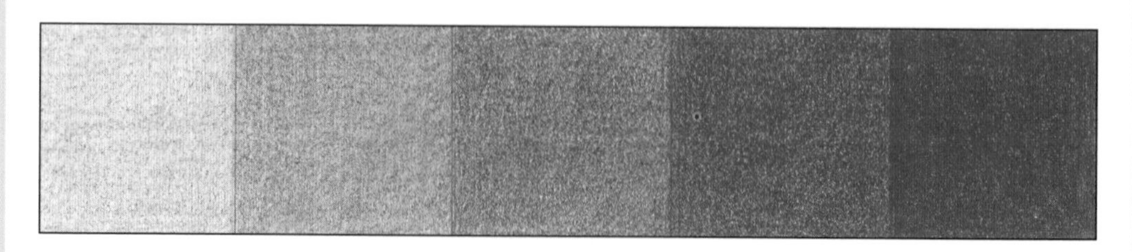

Value Scale
Making your own value scale will help familiarise you with the variations in value you can produce with a pencil. The scale also serves as a guide for transitioning from lighter to darker shades. Work from light to dark, adding more and more tone for successively darker values.

Basic Techniques

Below are examples of some of the most basic colouring techniques that you can use to replicate everything from smooth hair to rough wood. As you get your skills into shape, you can experiment and try new techniques. Whatever techniques you use, though, remember to shade evenly. Shading in a mechanical, side-to-side direction, with each stroke ending below the last, can create unwanted bands of tone throughout the shaded area. Instead, try shading evenly, in a back-and-forth motion over the same area, varying the spot where the pencil (marker, crayon) point changes direction.

Hatching
For this basic shading method, fill an area with a series of parallel strokes. The closer the strokes, the darker the tone will be.

Crosshatching
For darker shading, place layers of parallel strokes on top of one another at varying angles.

Shading Darkly
Apply heavy pressure to the pencil to create dark, linear areas of shading.

Gradating
Apply heavy pressure with the side of your pencil, gradually lightening as you go.

Colour Basics

Knowing basic colour theory can help you when drawing with coloured pencils. The *primary colours* (red, yellow and blue) are the three basic colours that can't be created by mixing other colours; all other colours are derived from these three. *Secondary colours* (orange, green and purple) are each a combination of two primaries, and *tertiary colours* (red–orange, red–purple, yellow–orange, yellow–green, blue–green and blue–purple) are a combination of a primary colour and a secondary colour.

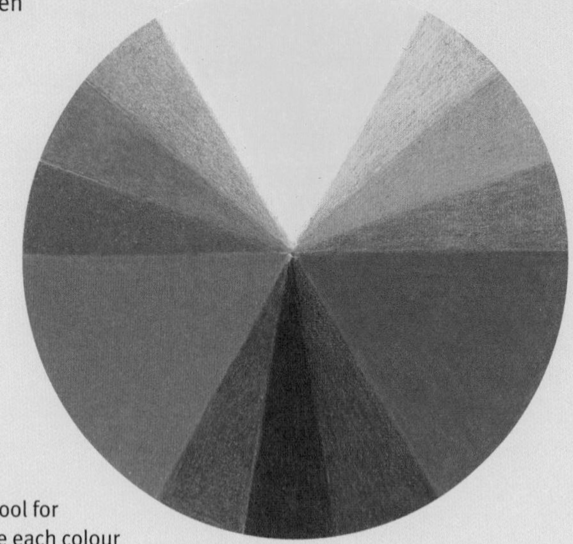

Colour Wheel A colour wheel is a useful reference tool for understanding colour relationships. Knowing where each colour lies on the colour wheel makes it easy to understand how colours relate to and react with one another.

Complementary Colours

Complementary colours are any two colours directly across from each other on the colour wheel (such as red and green, orange and blue, or yellow and purple). You can actually see combinations of complementary colours in nature – for instance, if you look at white clouds in a blue sky, you'll notice a hint of orange in the clouds.

Using Complements When placed next to each other, complementary colours create lively, exciting contrasts. Using a complementary colour in the background will cause your subject to seemingly 'pop' off the paper. For example, you could place bright orange poppies against a blue sky or draw red berries amid green leaves.

Colour Psychology

Colours are often referred to in terms of 'temperature', but that doesn't mean actual heat. An easy way to understand colour temperature is to think of the colour wheel as divided into two halves: The colours on the red side are warm and the colours on the blue side are cool. So colours with red or yellow in them appear warmer and colours with more green or blue in them appear cooler. For instance, if a normally cool colour (like green) has more yellow added to it, it will appear warmer; and if a warm colour (like red) has a little more blue, it will seem cooler. Another point to remember about colour temperature is that warm colours appear to come forward and cool colours appear to recede; this knowledge is valuable when creating the illusion of depth in a scene.

Warm Versus Cool Here the same scene is drawn with two different palettes: one warm (below) and one cool (top). Notice that the mood is strikingly different in each scene. This is because colour arouses certain feelings; for example, warm colours generally convey energy and excitement, whereas cooler colours usually indicate calmness.

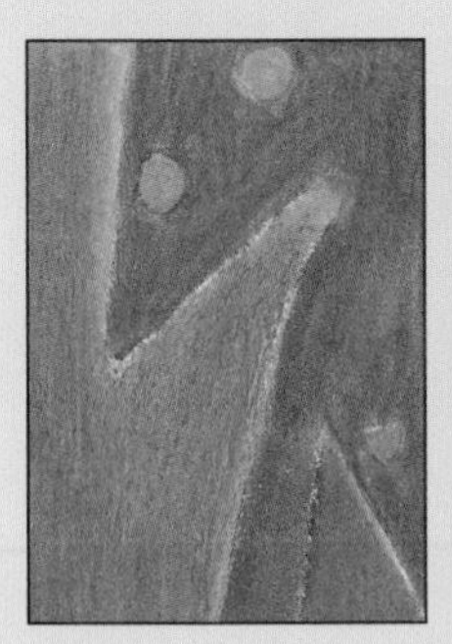

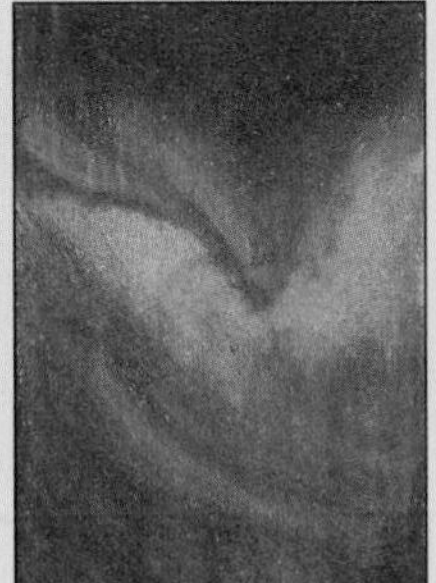

Colour Mood The examples here further illustrate how colour can be used to create mood (left to right): Complements can create a sense of tension; cool hues can evoke a sense of mystery; light, cool colours can evoke tranquility; and warm colours can create a sense of danger.

Tints, Shades and Tones

Colours can be tinted with white to make them lighter, shaded with black to make them darker or toned with grey to make them more muted. Here each colour was applied using graduated pressure – light, then heavy, then light. Black was applied at the top and white at the bottom to tint and tone the colours, respectively. To tint a colour without muting it, apply the white first and then the colour.

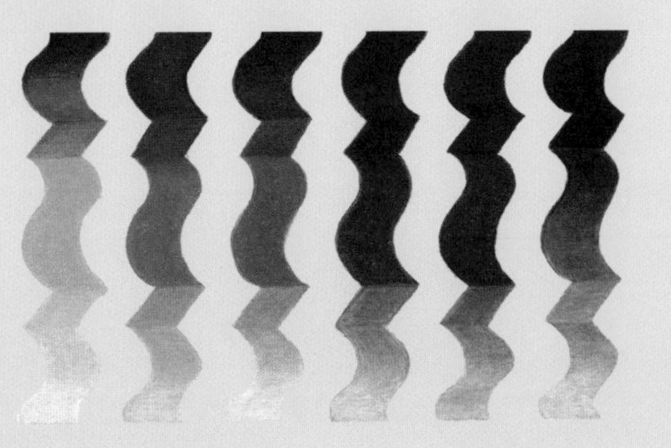

CHAPTER 1

Animals and Nature

1 Bees and Insects

Everyone's buzzing about this section – it's the bee's knees.

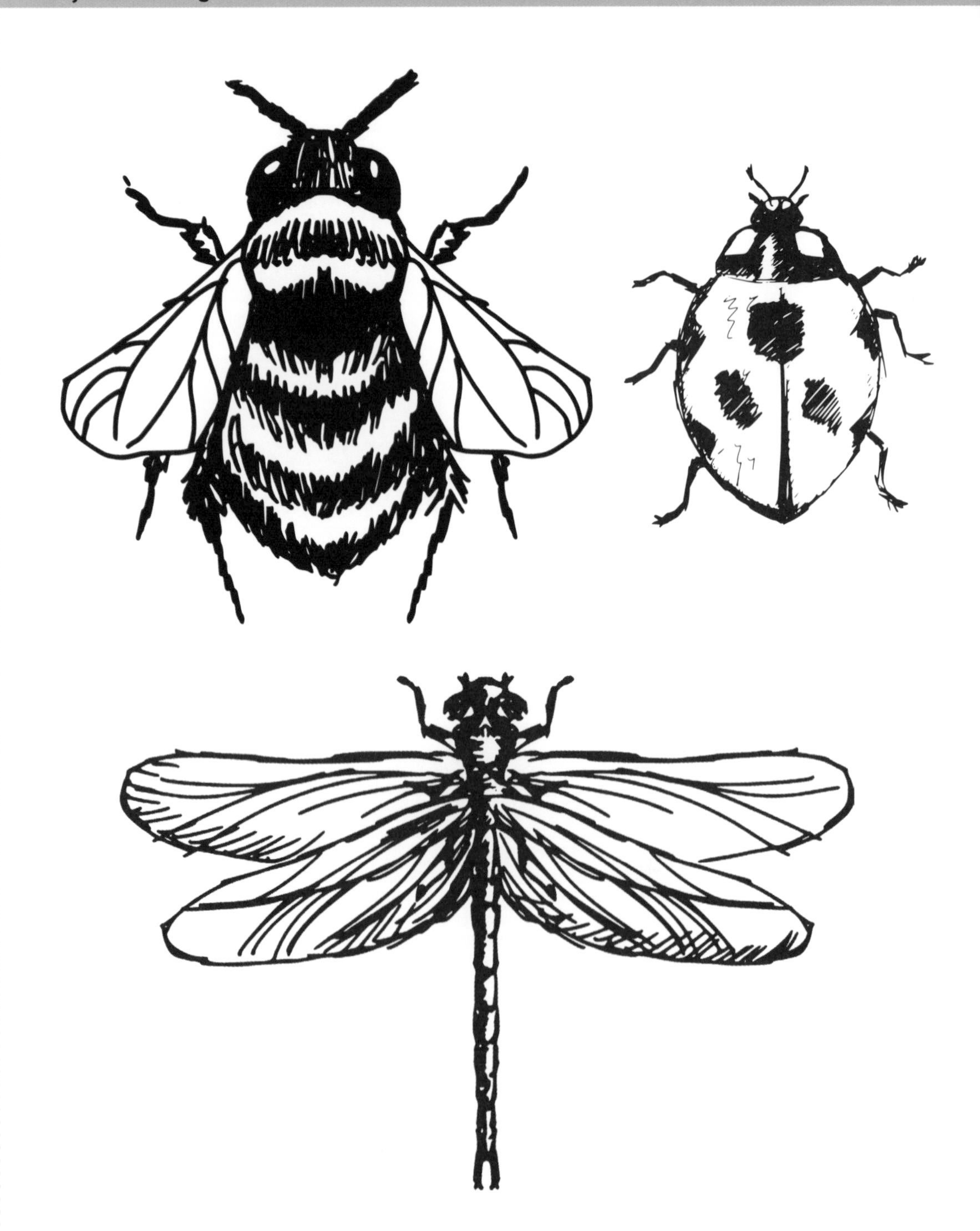

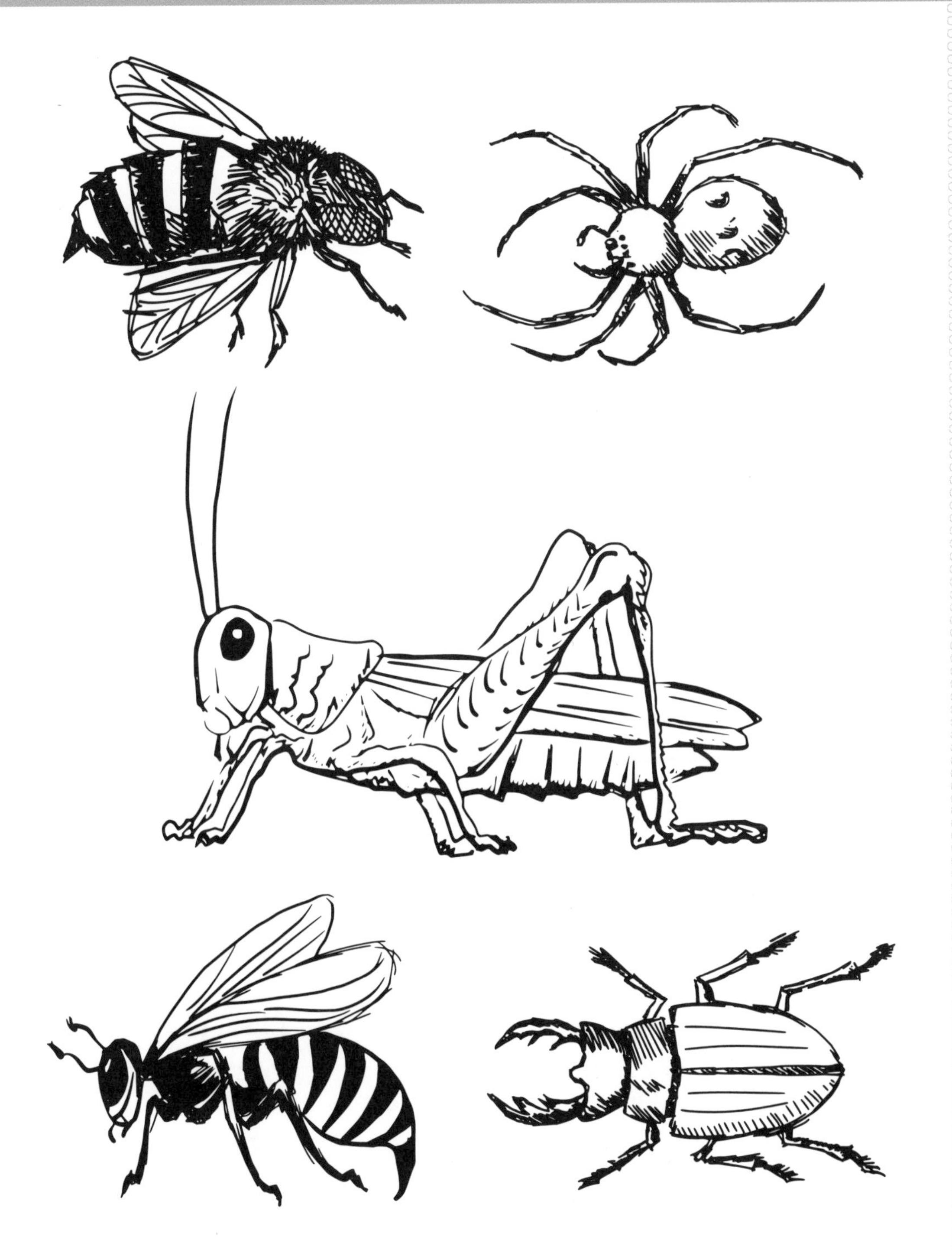

Colour
this
Pattern

2 Under the Sea

Dive into colour with these underwater creatures.

Colour
this
Pattern

3 Roaming the Forest

Little Red Riding Hood might have encountered creatures like these – beware of the big bad wolf!

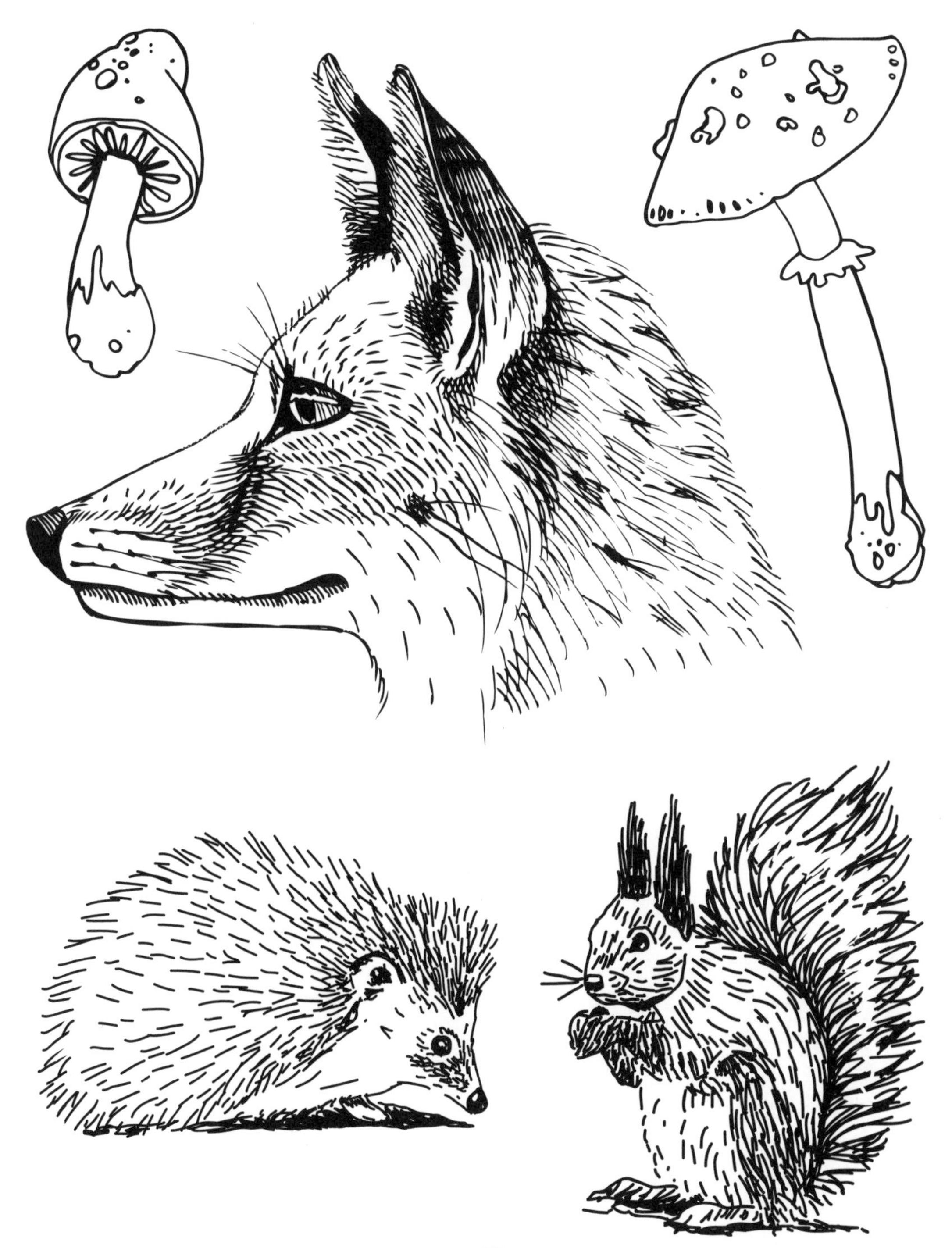

Colour this Pattern

4 Into the Wild

Roar and explore the habitat of these wild animals.

Colour
this
Pattern

5 Birds

Birds of a feather flock to colour.

Colour
this
Pattern

6 Four-Legged Friends

Cats and dogs do get along – when you colour them together.

Colour this Pattern

7 Trees

Once you've leafed through this book, why not come back and colour these trees?

Colour
this
Pattern

8 Succulents

Even in the desert, succulents bring a pop of colour.

Colour
this
Pattern

9 Flowers

Ever been told not to pick the flowers? Pick one here – or pick all of them – to colour.

Colour this Pattern

10 Butterflies

Flutter along with these fantastic creatures.

Colour
this
Pattern

11 Space

String theory holding the universe together? I think we're unified by colour.

Colour
this
Pattern

CHAPTER 2

People and Fashion

12 Coats

Zip up. Button down. Get colouring!

Colour
this
Pattern

13 Travel Bags

Pack up and let's get ready for the next adventure.

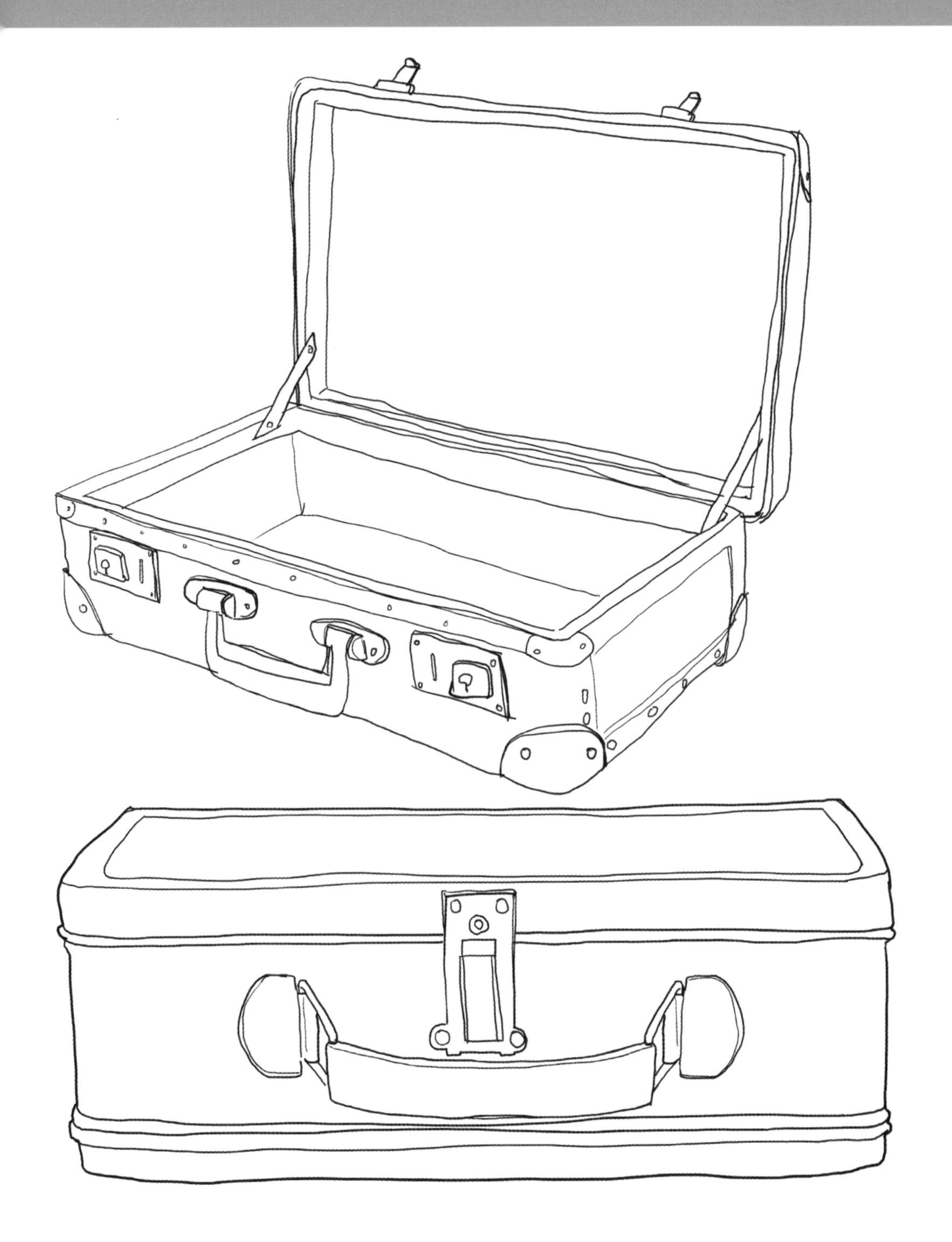

Colour
this
Pattern

14 Shoes

You know what they say: When the shoe fits... colour it!

Colour this Pattern

15 Hats

From bonnet to fedora, nothing tops a good hat!

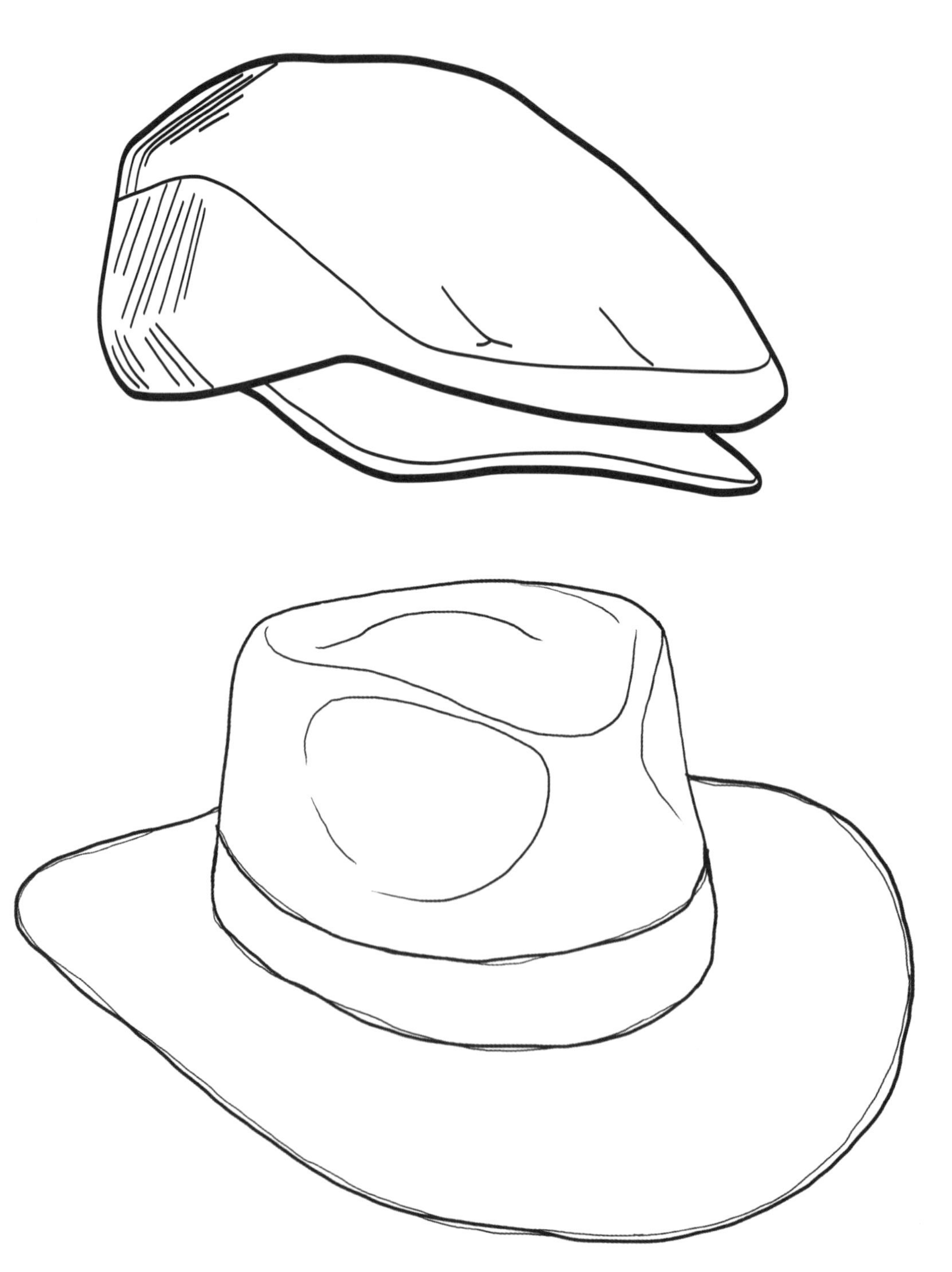

Colour
this
Pattern

16 Rain Gear

Splish splash! Bundle up and grab your umbrella – we're in for rainy weather!

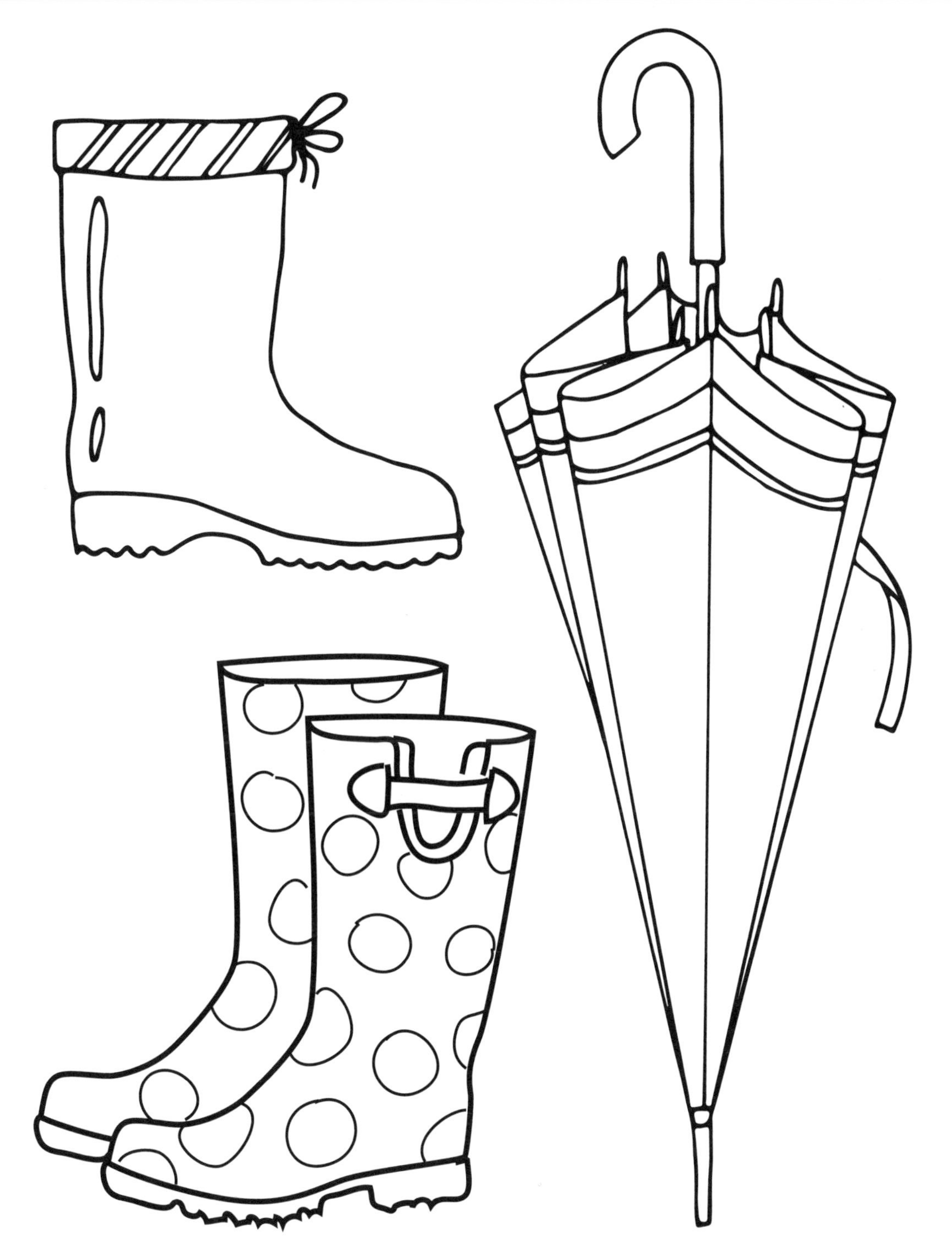

Colour this Pattern

17 Eveningwear

Definitely not just a black tie event.

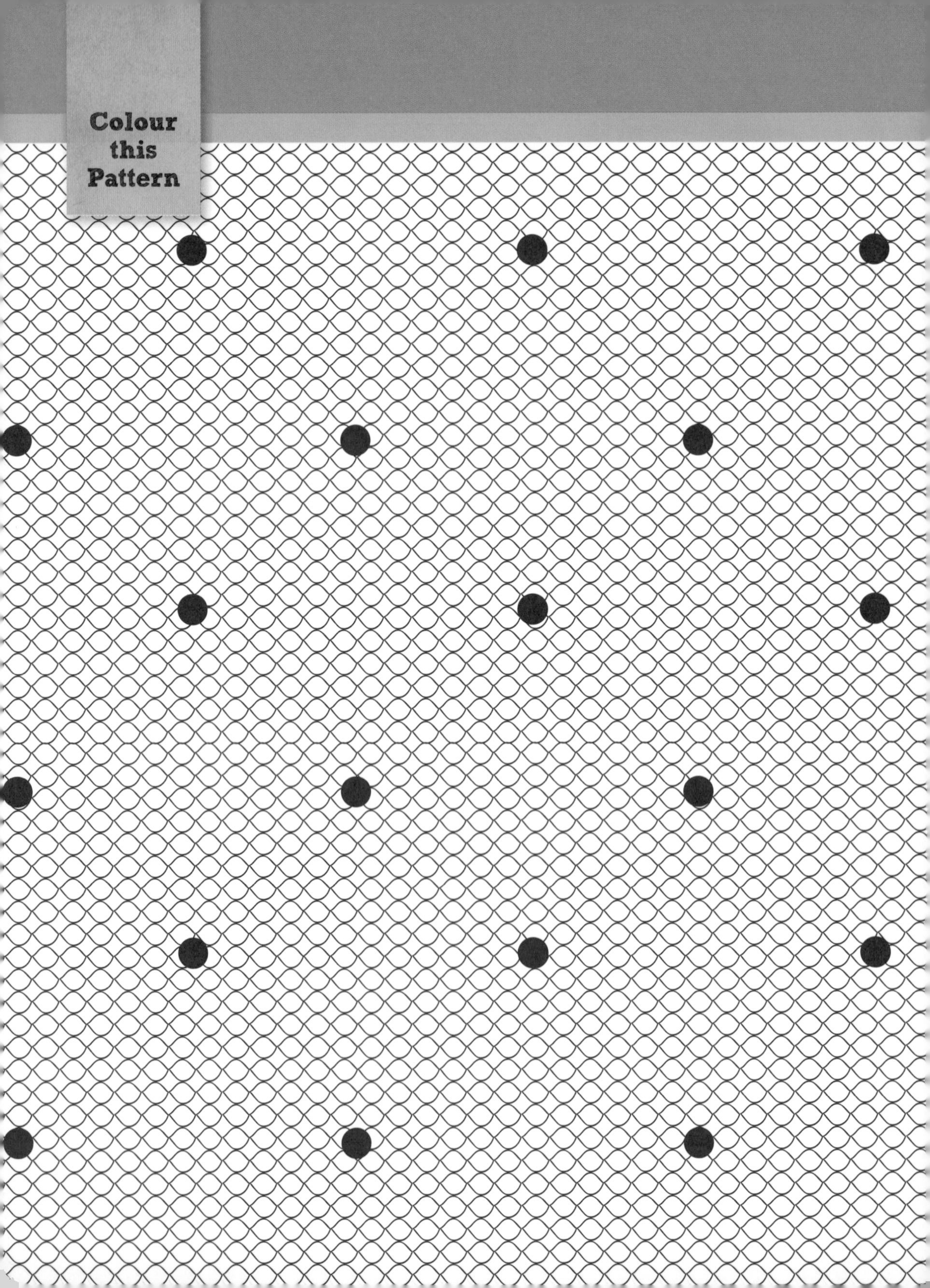
Colour
this
Pattern

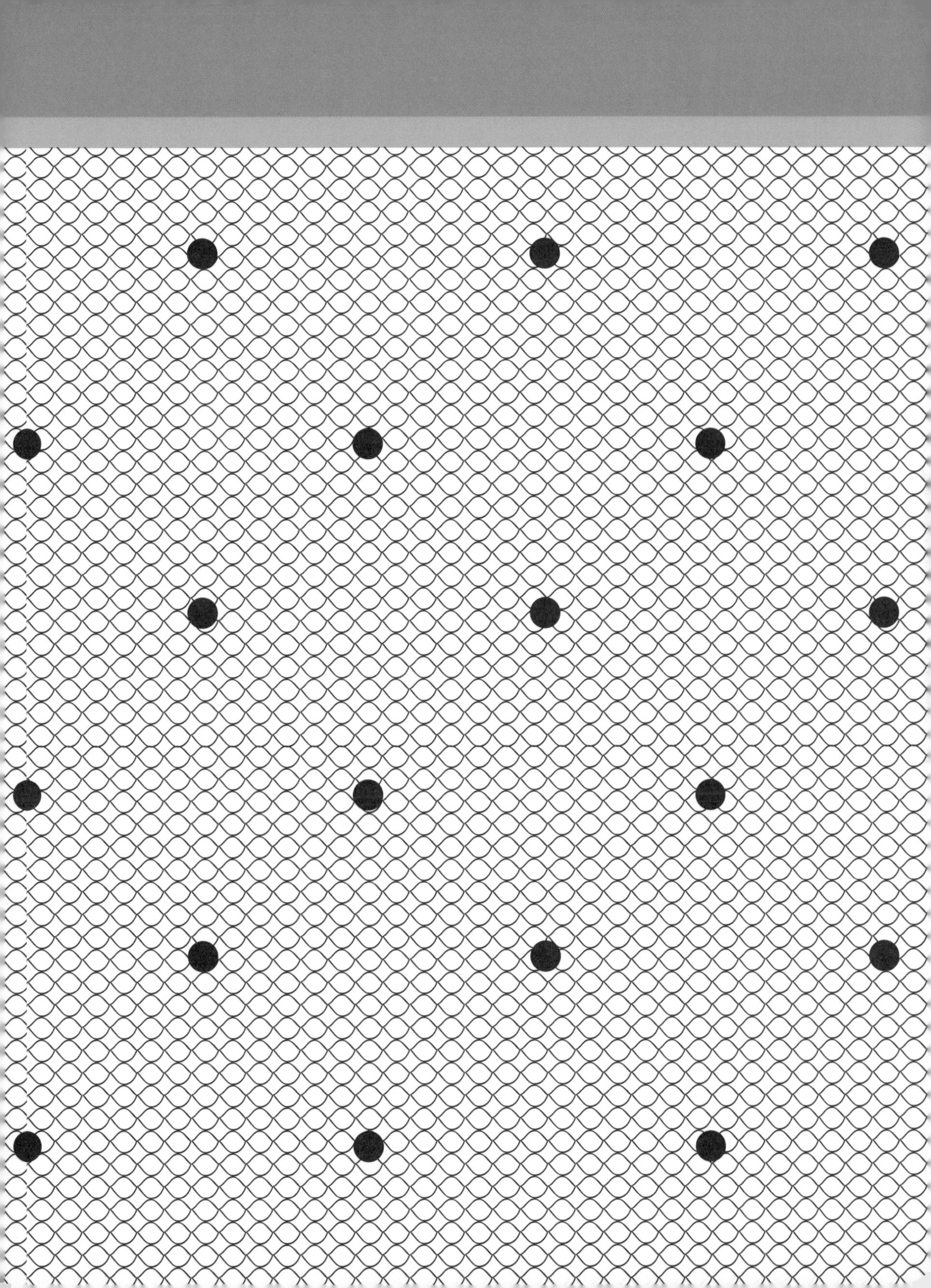

18 Fashion Studio

Sew colourful!

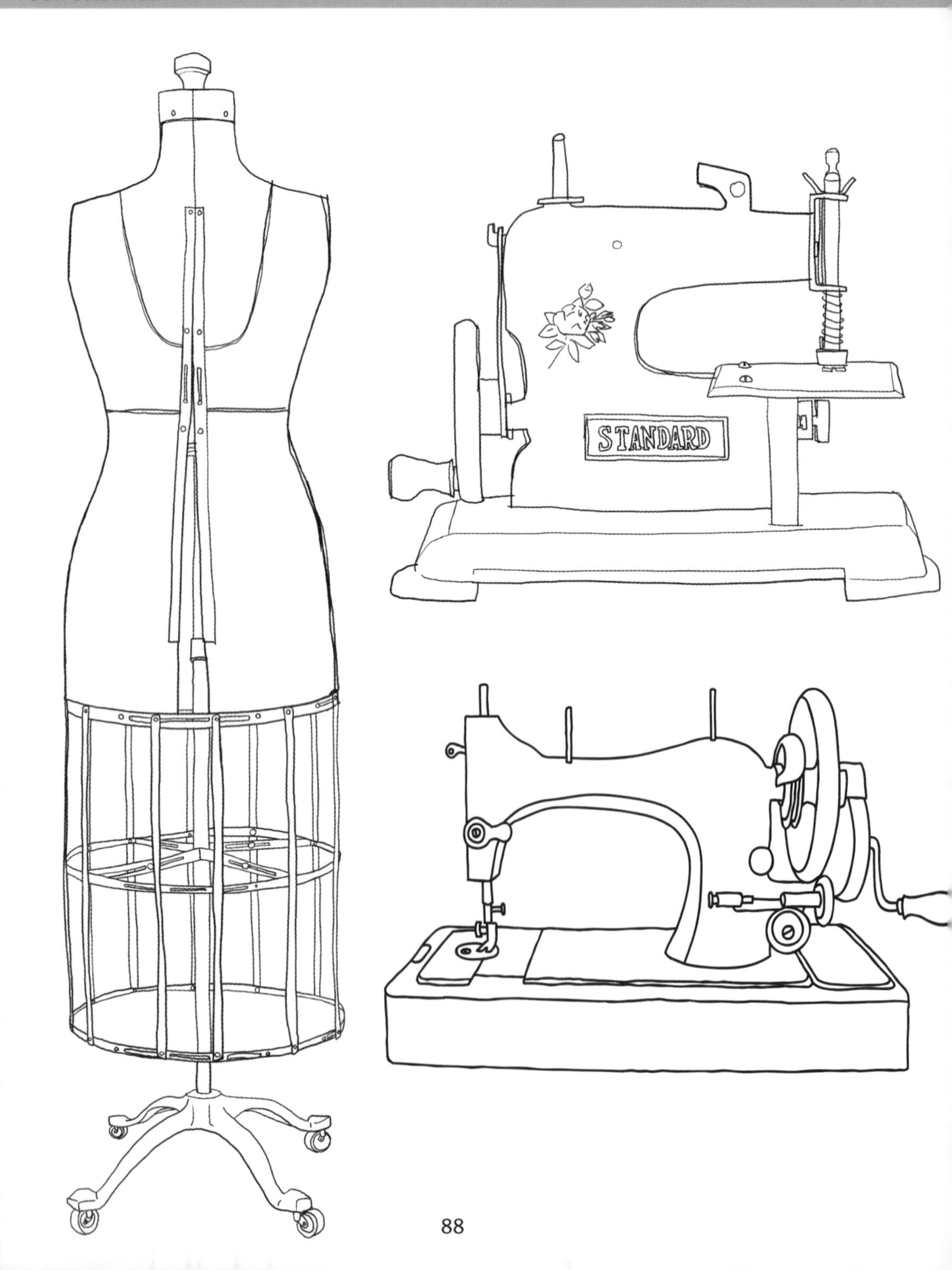

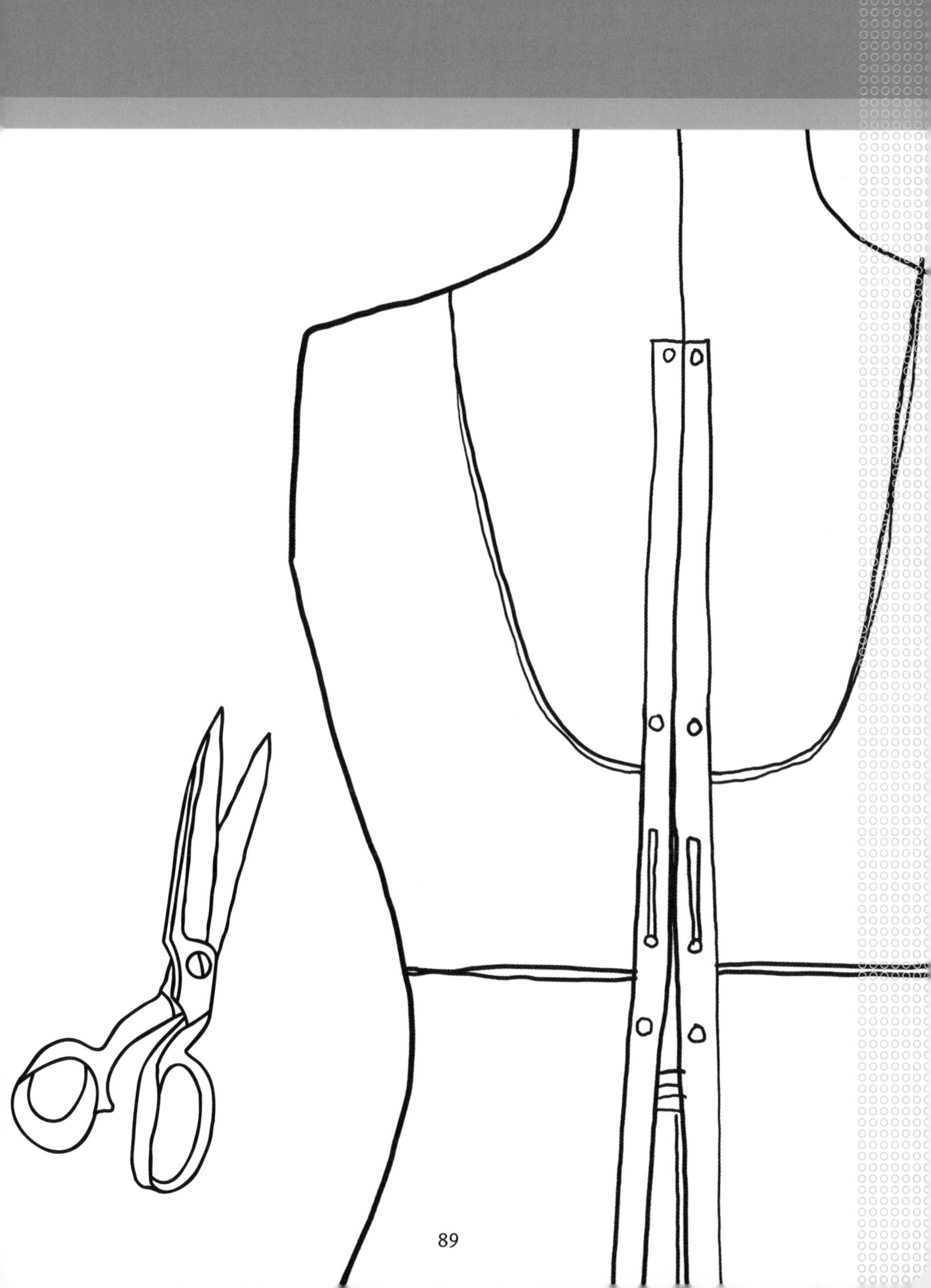

Colour this Pattern

CHAPTER 3

Food and Drink

19 Fruit

Tutti frutti!

Colour
this
Pattern

20 Vegetables

Not just good for you, they're also artistically interesting.

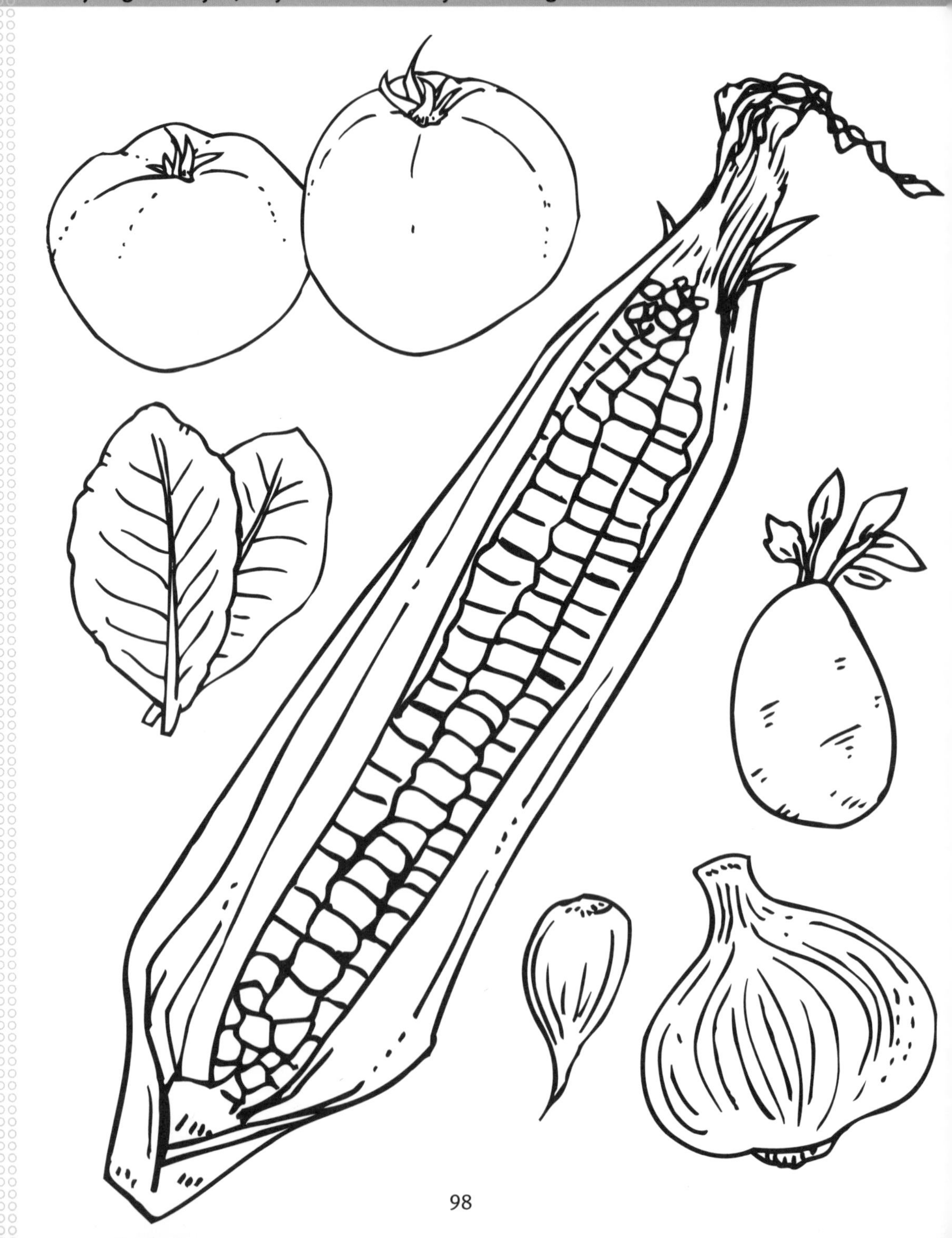

Colour
this
Pattern

21 Sushi Bar

Have a seat at the sushi bar and relax.

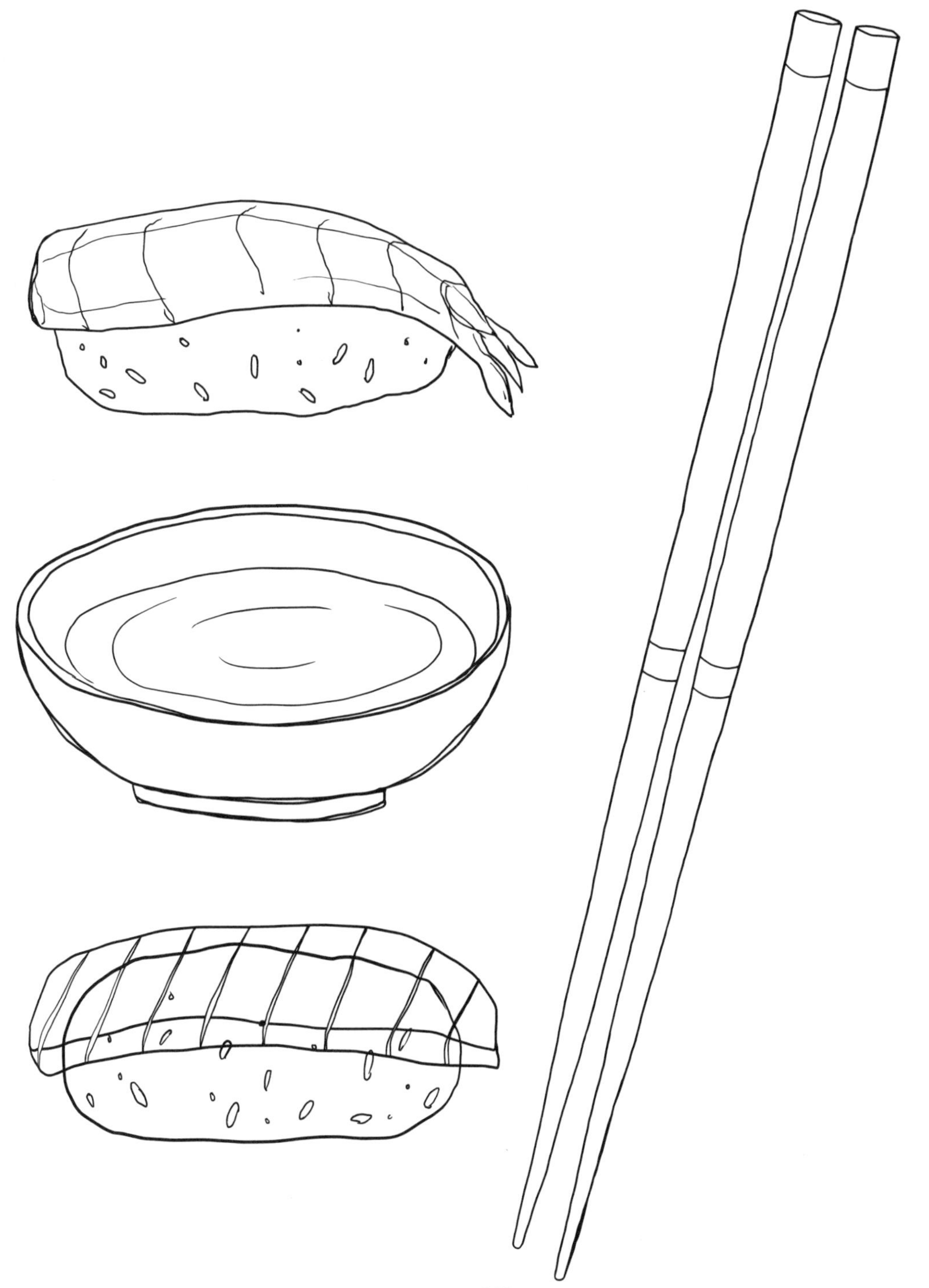

Colour
this
Pattern

22 Herbs and Spices

Flavour never looked so good!

Colour
this
Pattern

23 Coffee

Perk up with a colourful cup of the black stuff!

100
75
50
°C
ascoso

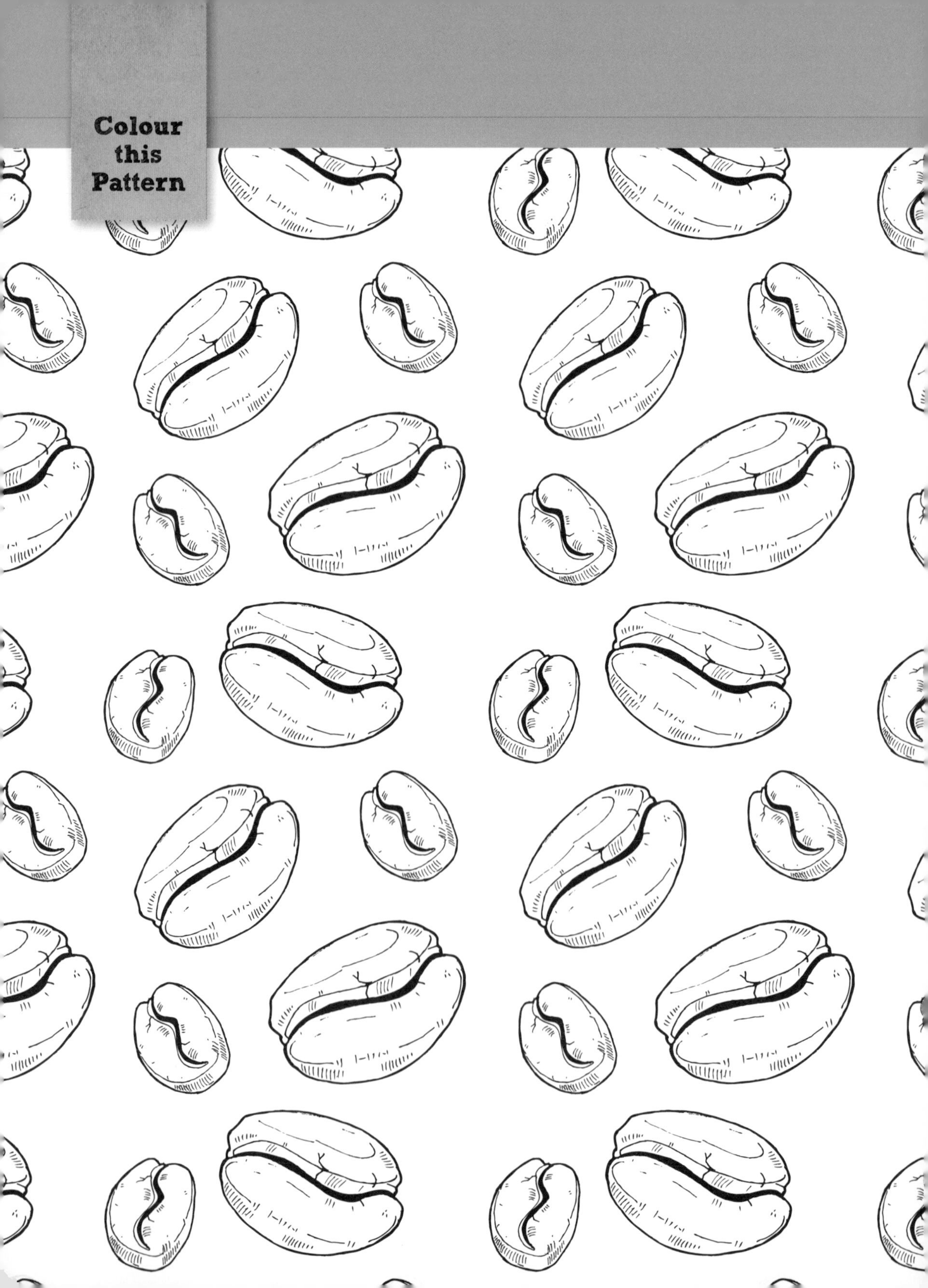
Colour this Pattern

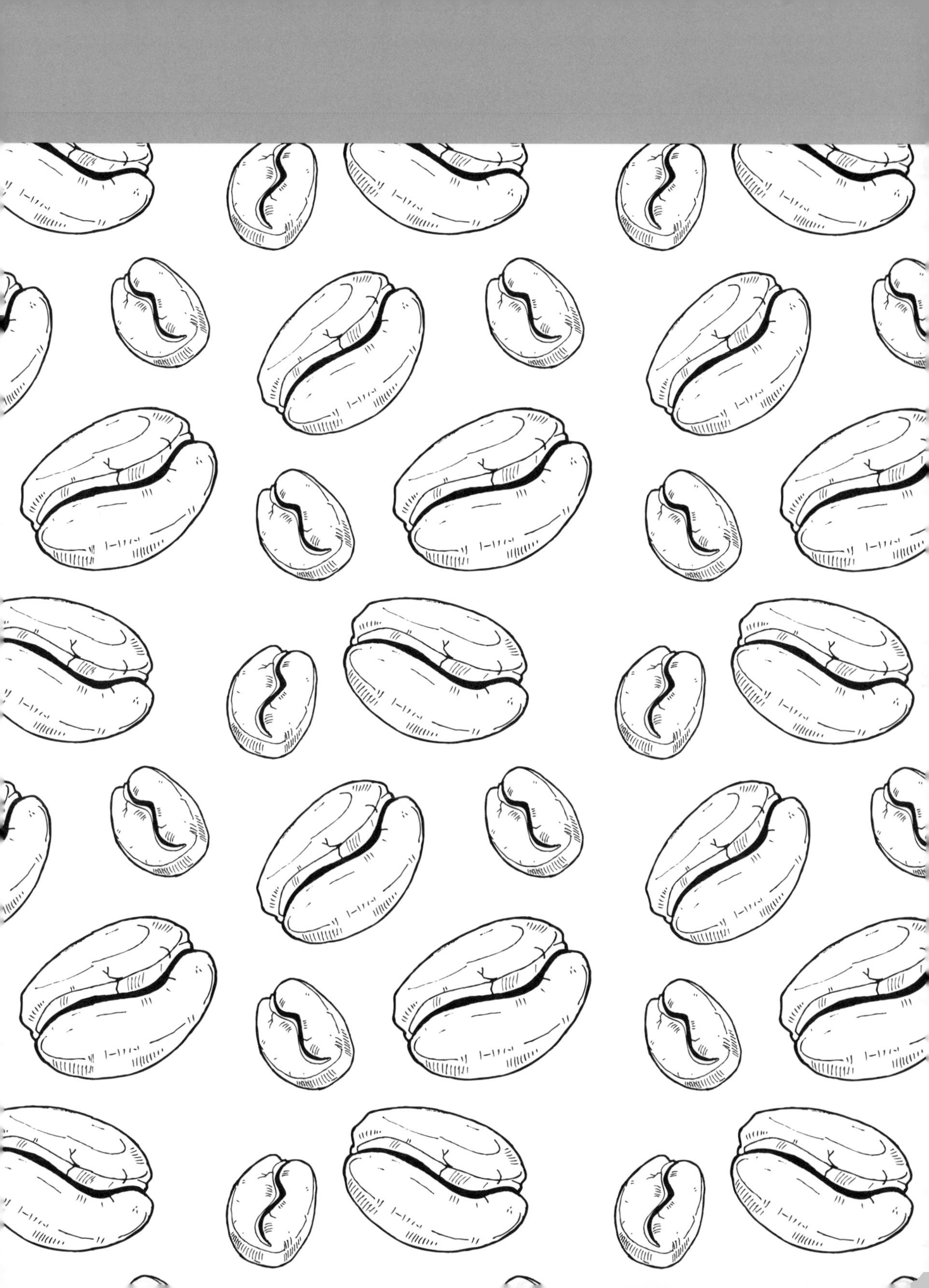

24 Ice Cream

Scoop me up a double chocolate banana split with extra hundreds and thousands.

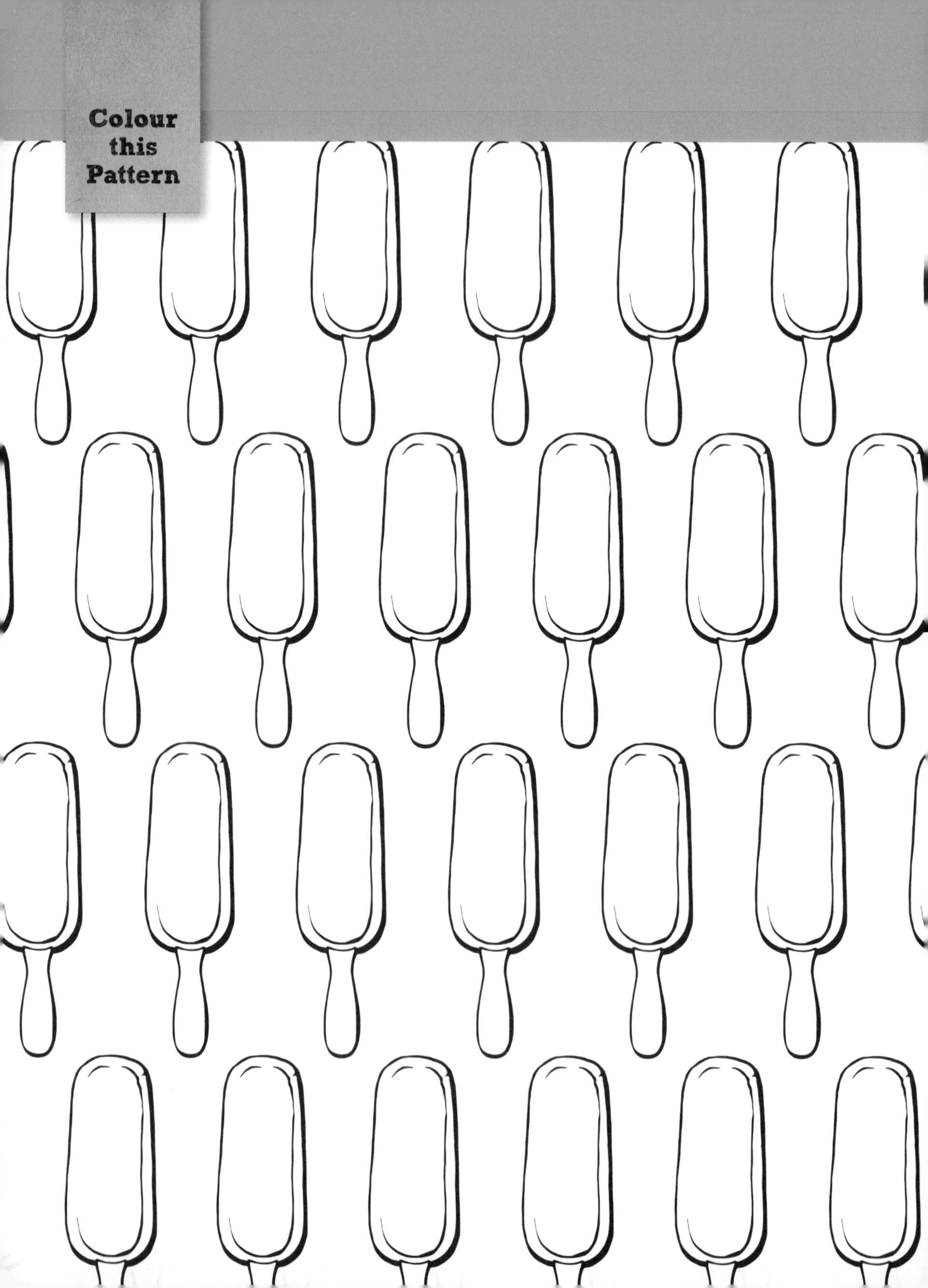
Colour this Pattern

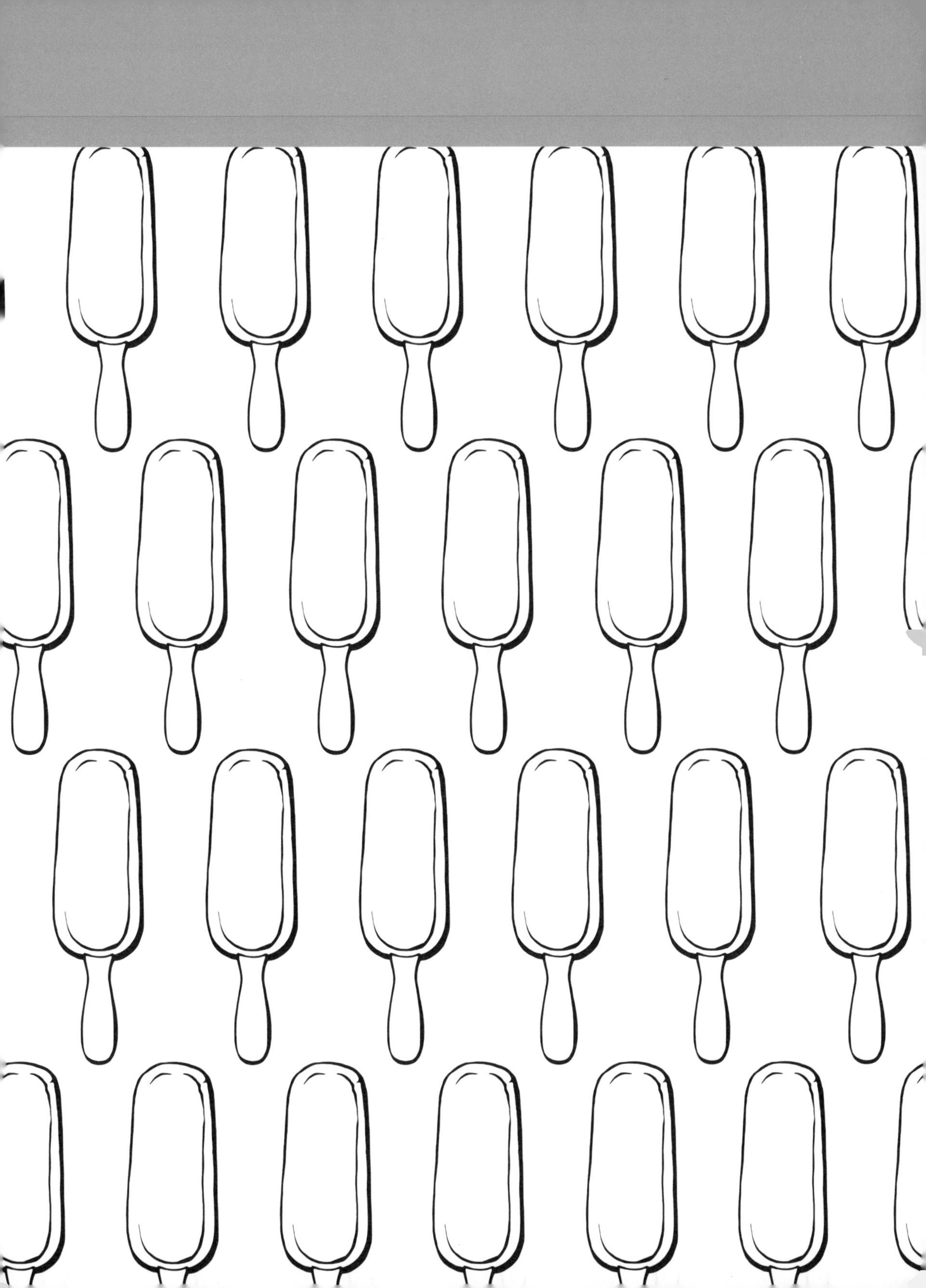

25 Noodles

Oodles of hued noodles.

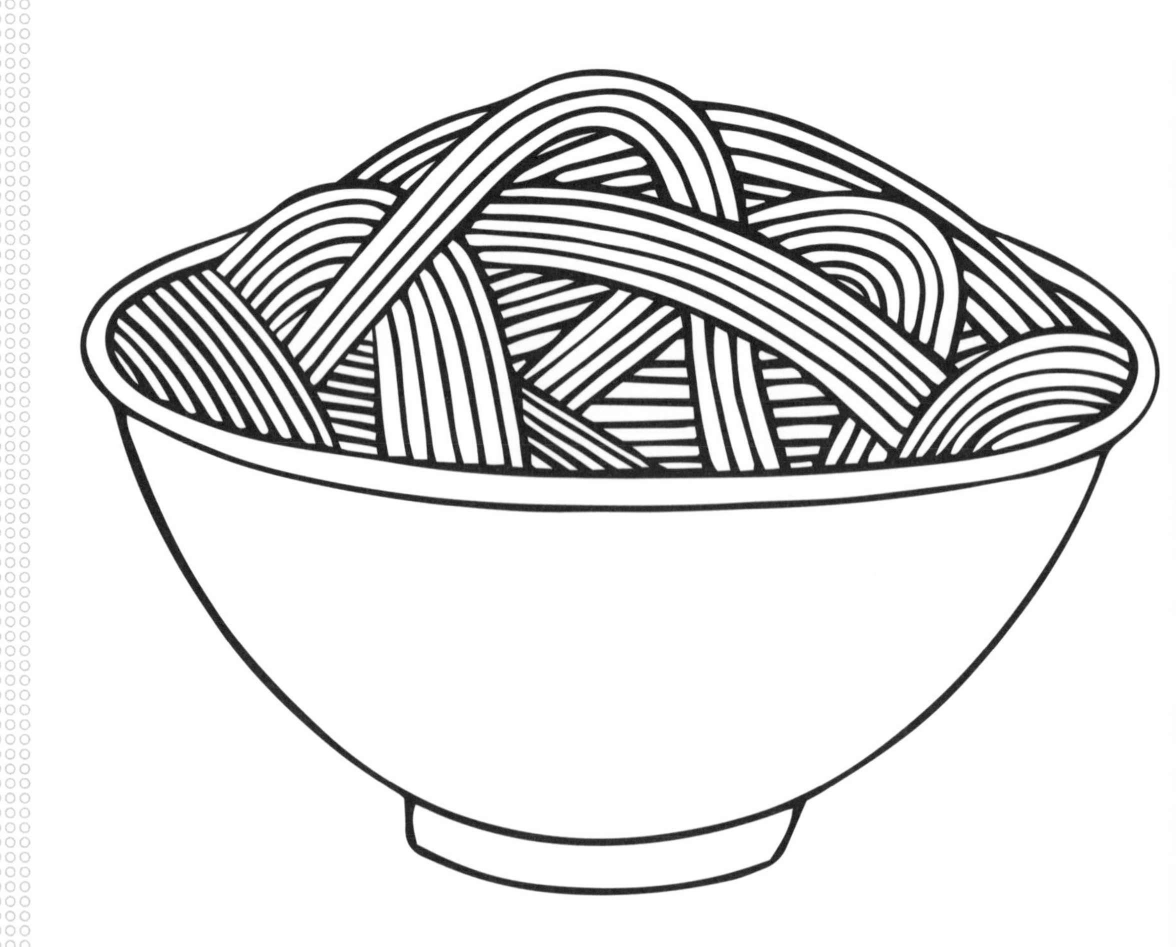

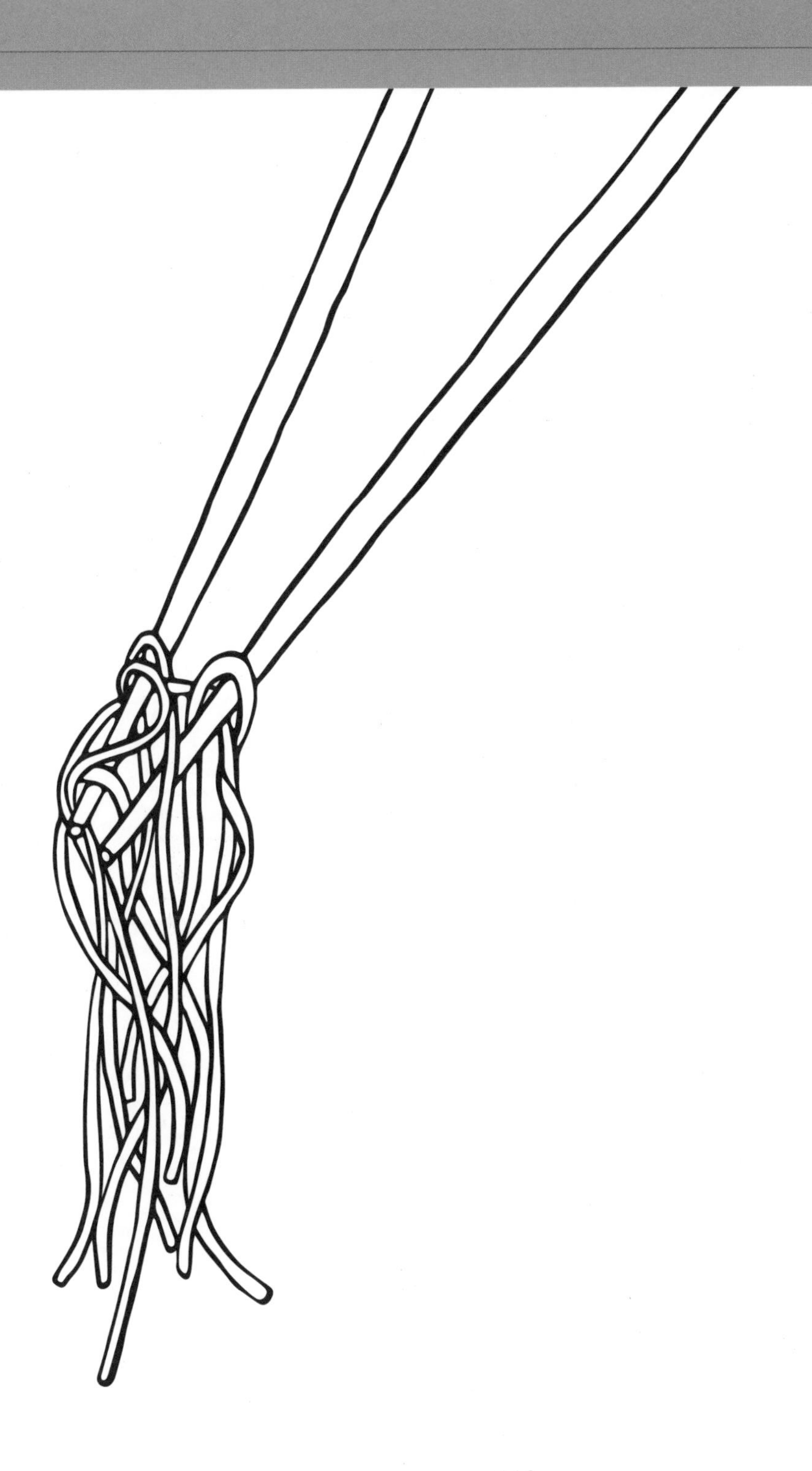

Colour
this
Pattern

26 Cupcakes

Guilt free! Enjoy all seven cupcakes – with no worries of calories.

Colour this Pattern

27 Sweets

I'm sweet on colour!

Colour
this
Pattern

28 Doughnuts

Mouthwatering doughnuts...now all I need is a cup of coffee for dunking.

Colour
this
Pattern

29 Wine and Bubbly

Bottoms up!

Colour
this
Pattern

Cocktails

Cheers to creativity!

Colour this Pattern

CHAPTER 4

Still Lifes and Other Objects

Tick. Tock. Colour a clock.

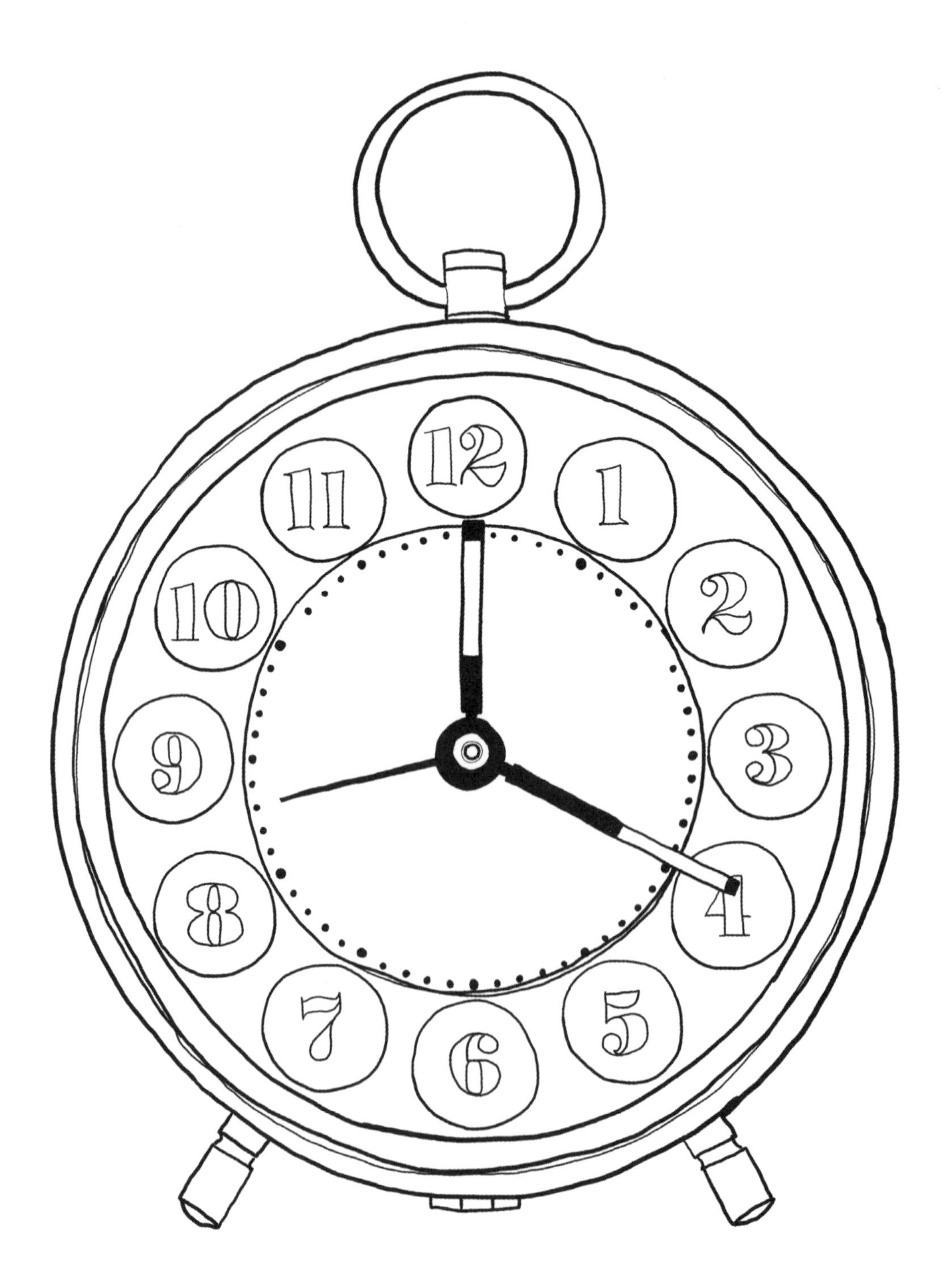

12
1
2
3
4
5
6
7
8
9
10
11

Colour this Pattern
12
11
1
10
2
9
3
8
4
7
6
5
60
50
10
40
20
30

32 Bicycles

Throw some markers in the basket, and let's ride.

Colour this Pattern

33 Typewriters

Ding! That's the sound to stop hammering on the keys – and get colouring these.

AUTOMATIC REPEAT SPACER
TAB
REPEAT SPACER
BACK SPACER
SHIFT LOCK
TAB
SHIFT KEY
SHIFT KEY

Colour this Pattern

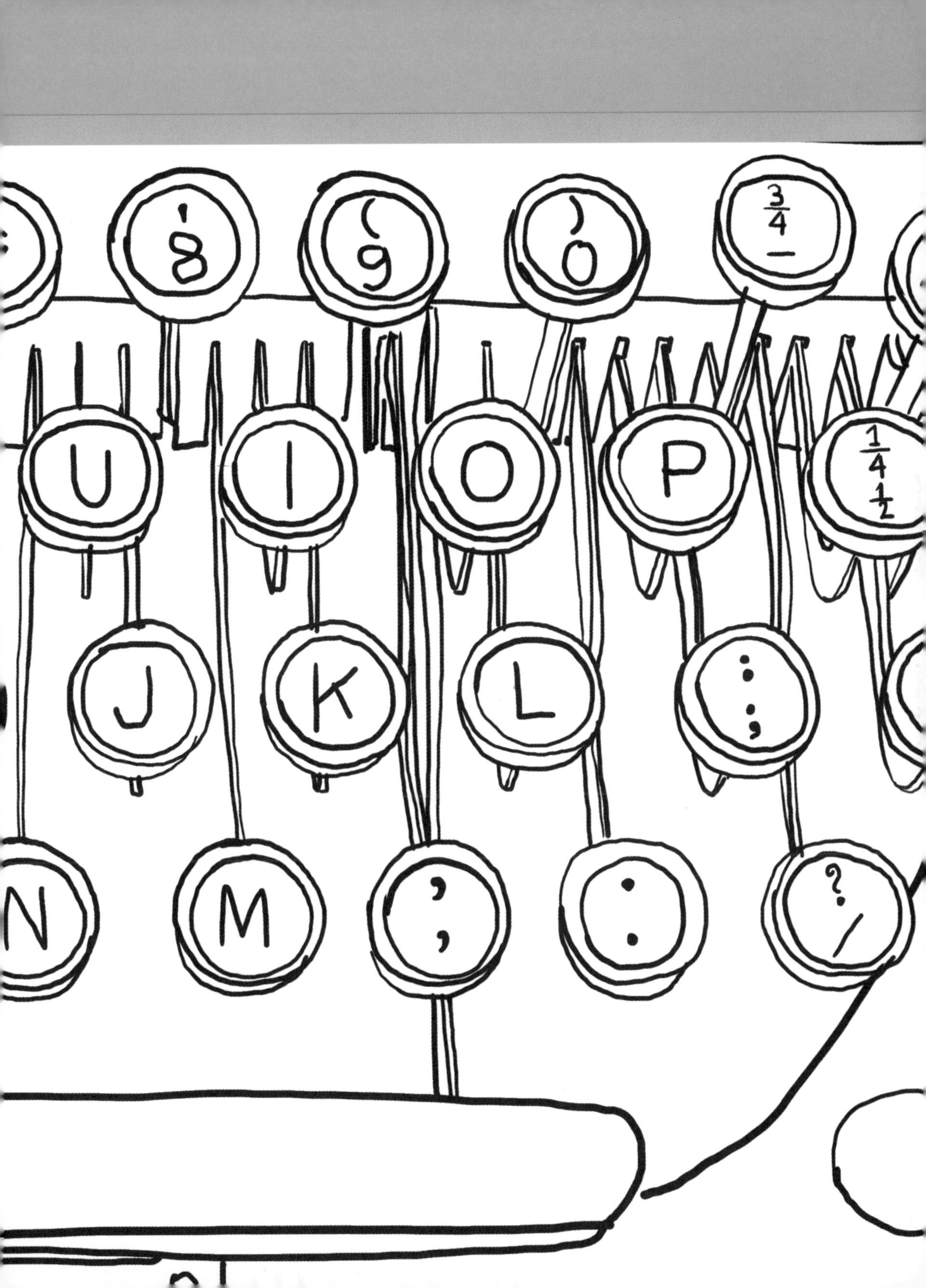

8
9
0
U
I
O
P
J
K
L
N
M

34 Vintage Music

Groove on the sounds of yesterday, today.

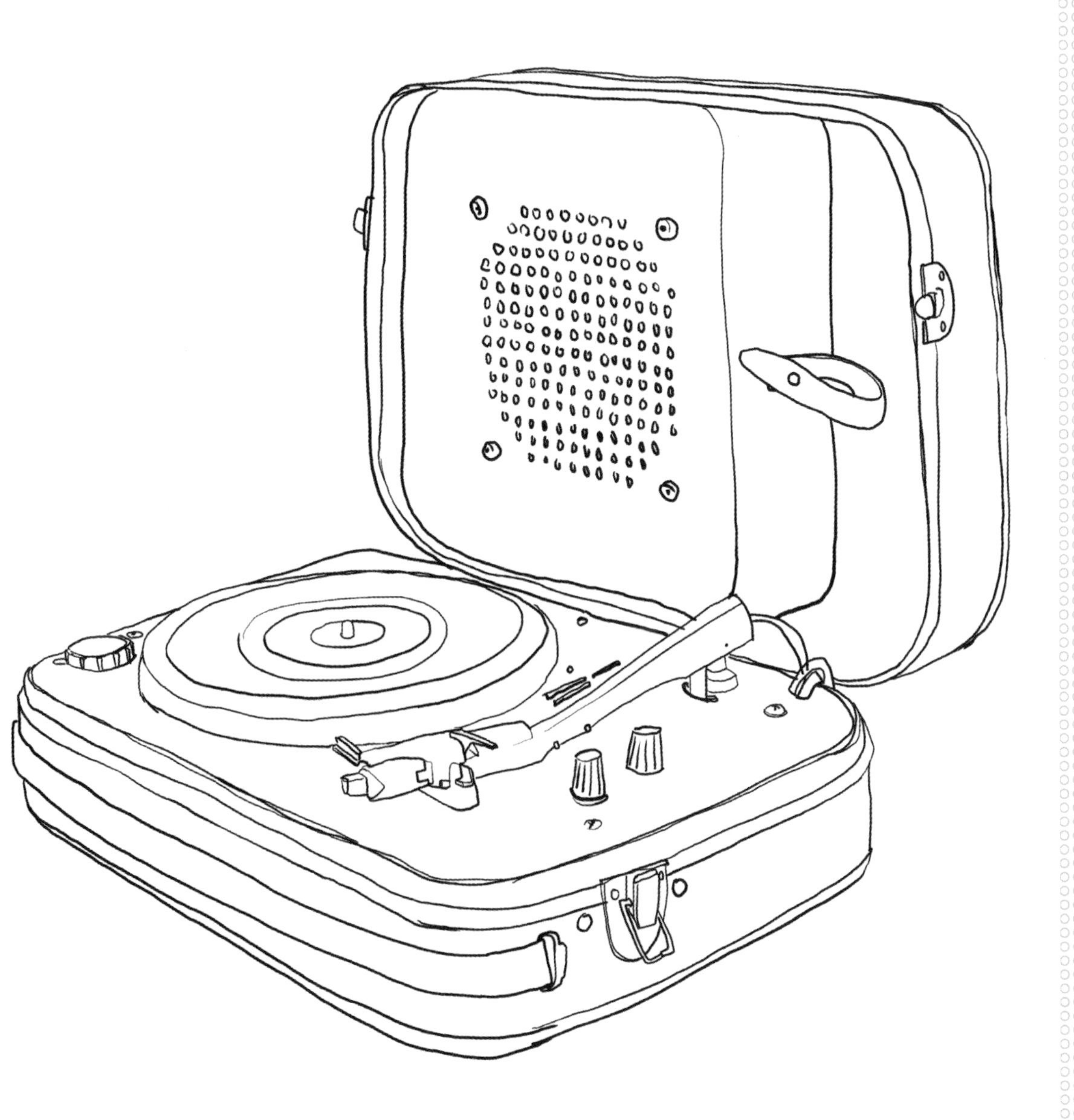

Colour
this
Pattern
1
1
1

35 Robots and Space Toys

Preprogrammed for a rainbow of robotic fun.

Colour this Pattern

36 Glasses

See the world through beautifully tinted specs.

Colour
this
Pattern

37 Cameras

The focus here is colour.

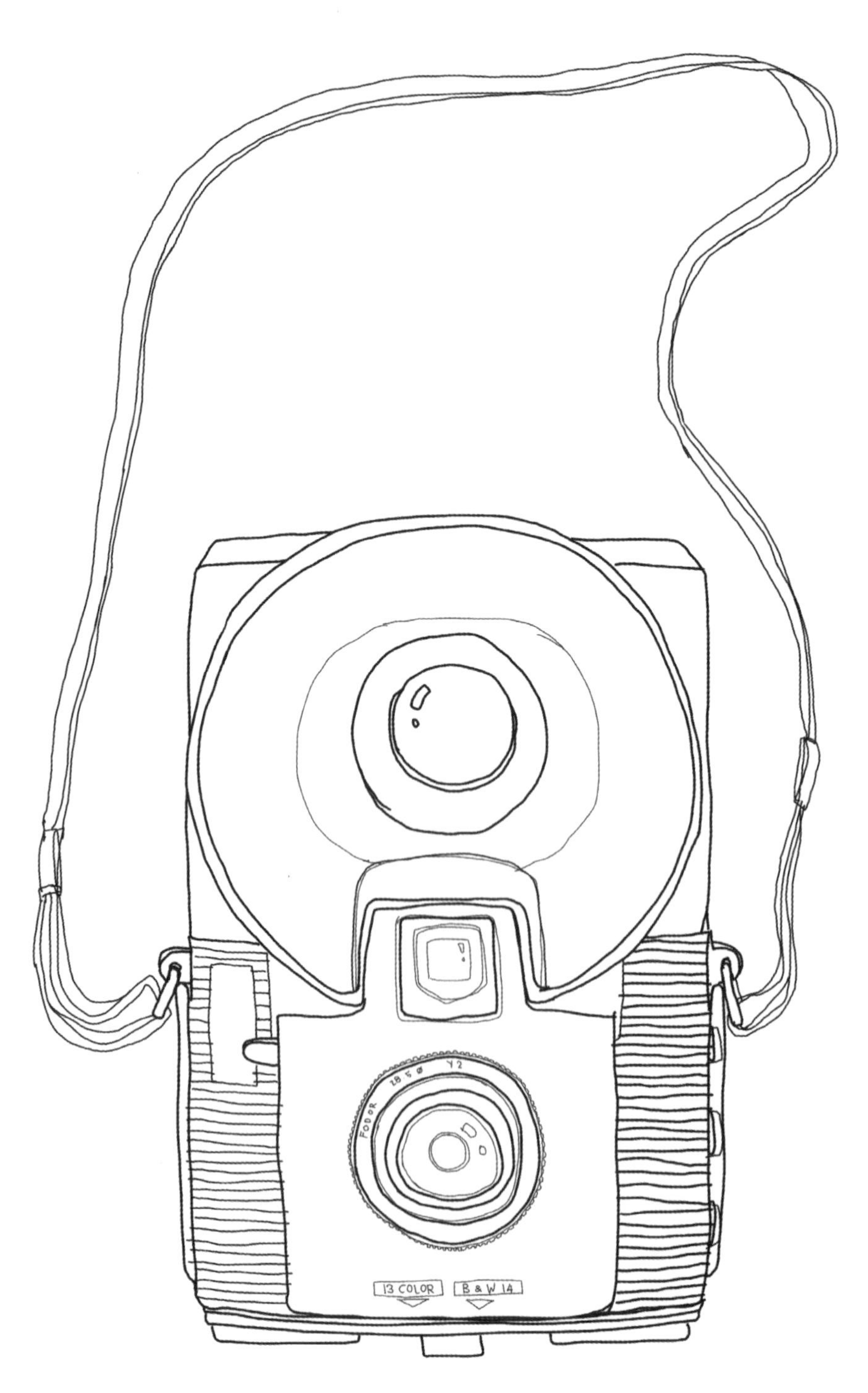

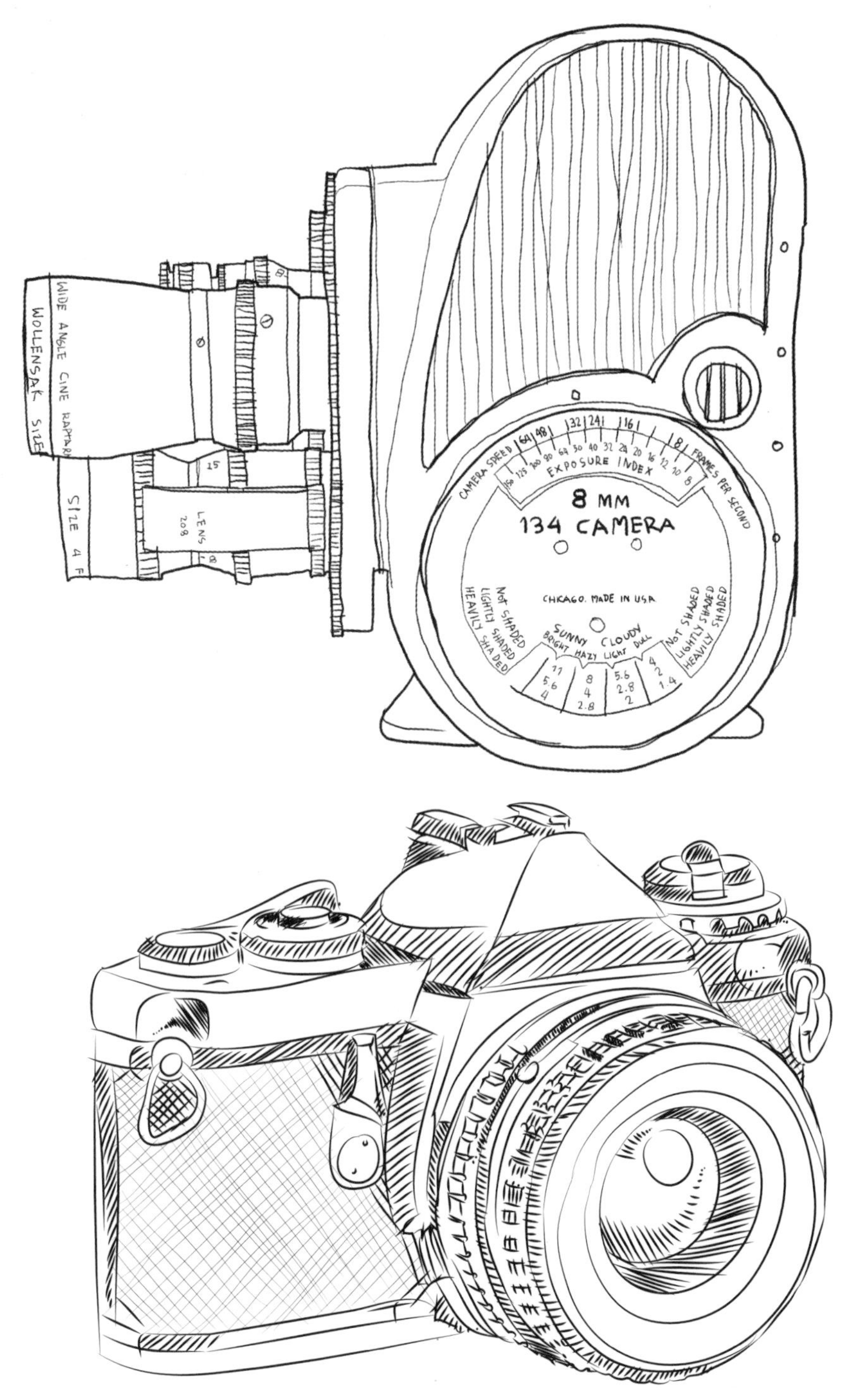

8 MM
134 CAMERA
CAMERA SPEED
EXPOSURE INDEX
FRAMES PER SECOND
CHICAGO. MADE IN USA
Not SHADED
LIGHTLY SHADED
HEAVILY SHADED
SUNNY
CLOUDY
BRIGHT
HAZY
LIGHT
DULL
NOT SHADED
LIGHTLY SHADED
HEAVILY SHADED
WIDE ANGLE CINE RAPTAR
WOLLENSAK

Colour
this
Pattern

38 Radios

Tune that dial and find the perfect station for colouring elation.

00
120
140
160
EAKERS

Colour
this
Pattern

39 Silverware and China

It's a formal dinner party, and every colour's invited.

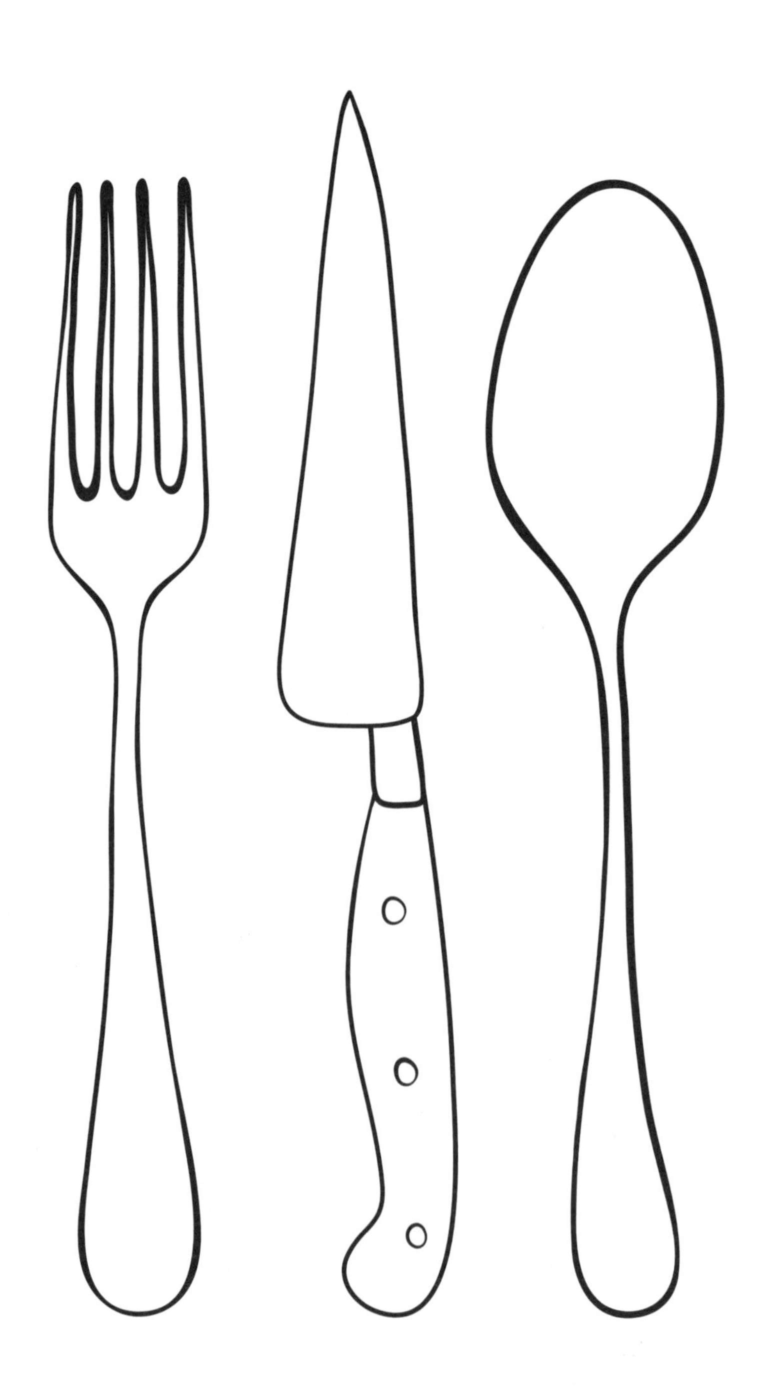

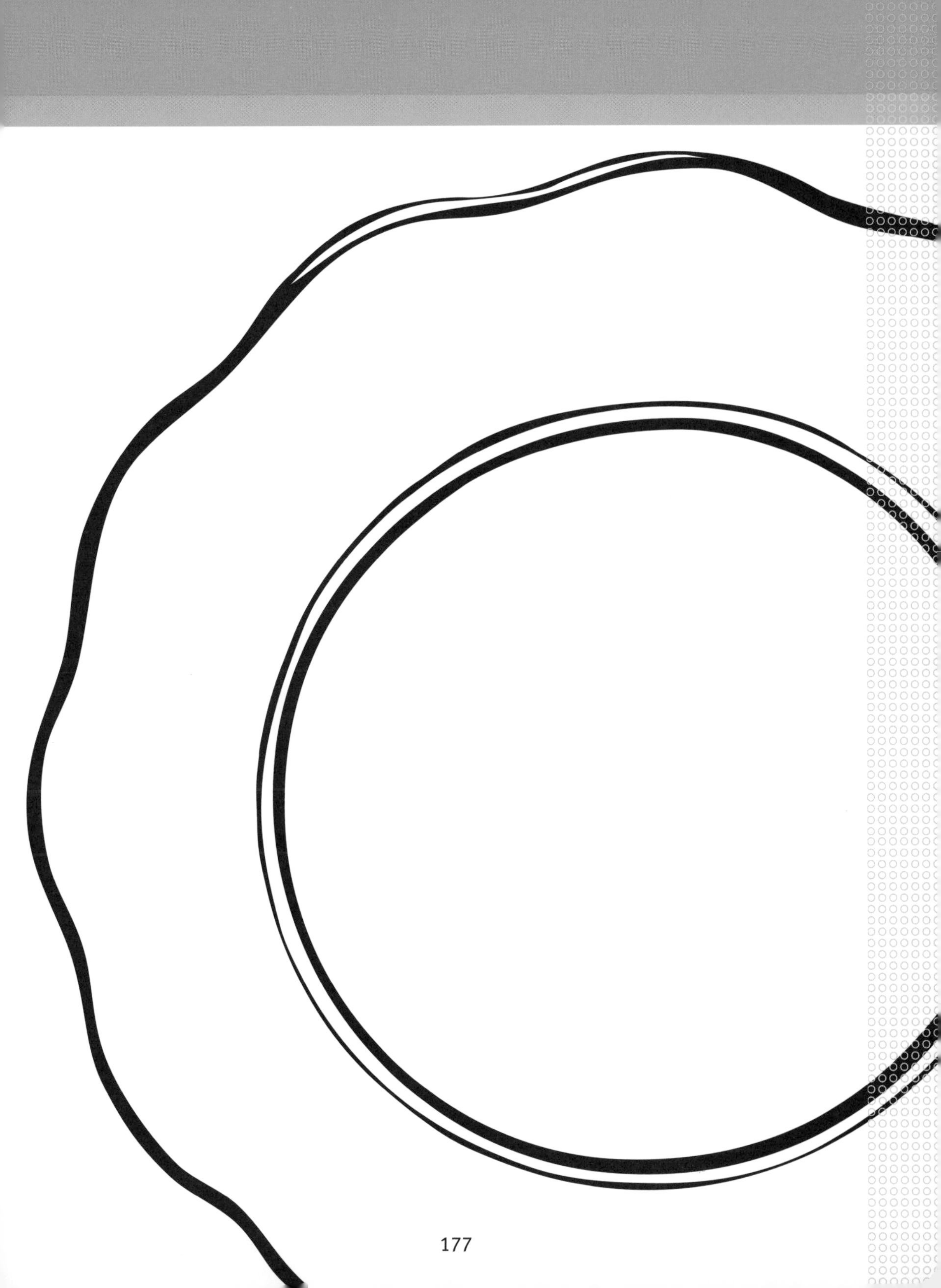

Colour
this
Pattern

Retro TVs

It's not a virtual wasteland if you're colouring TVs...

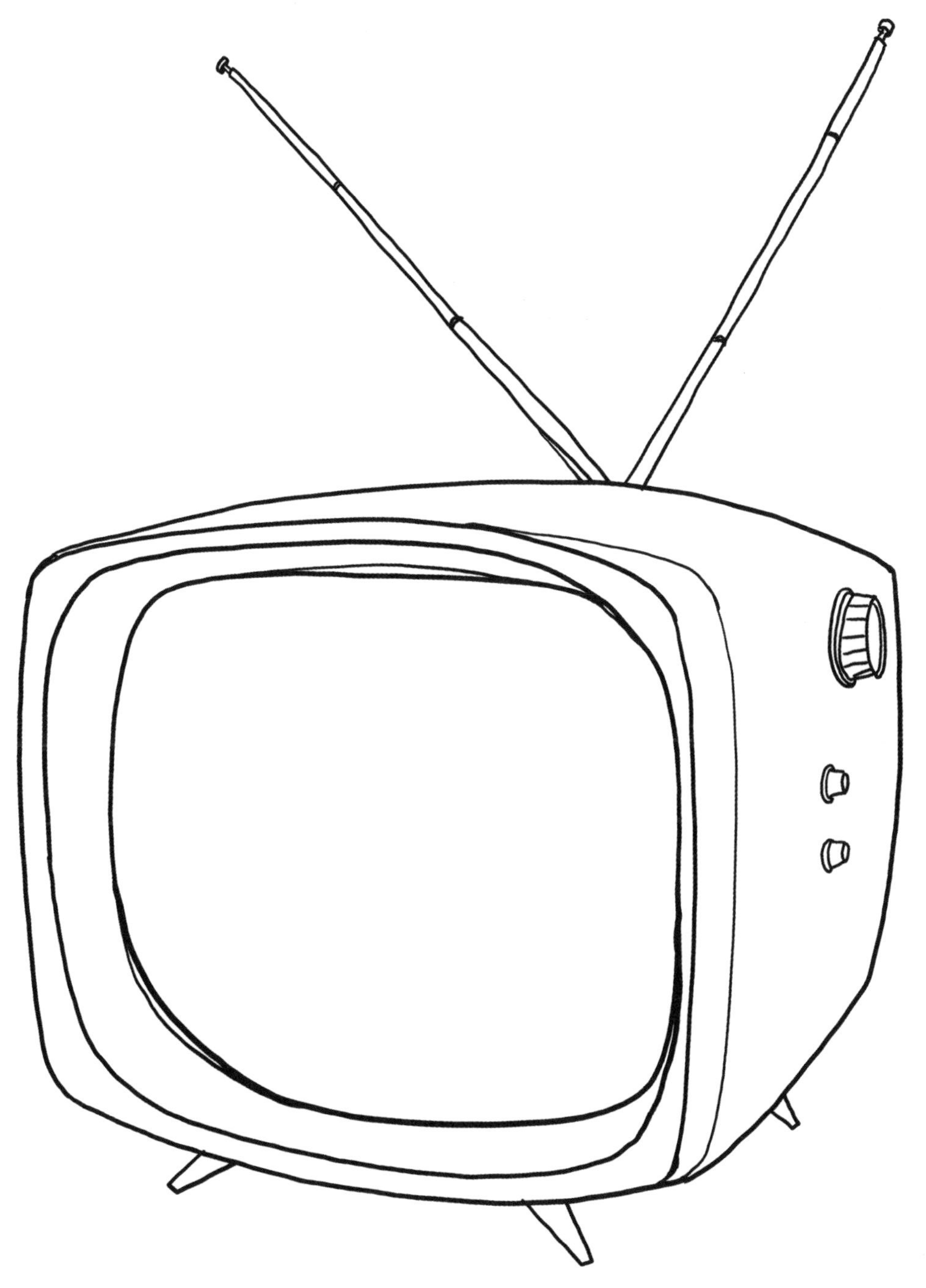

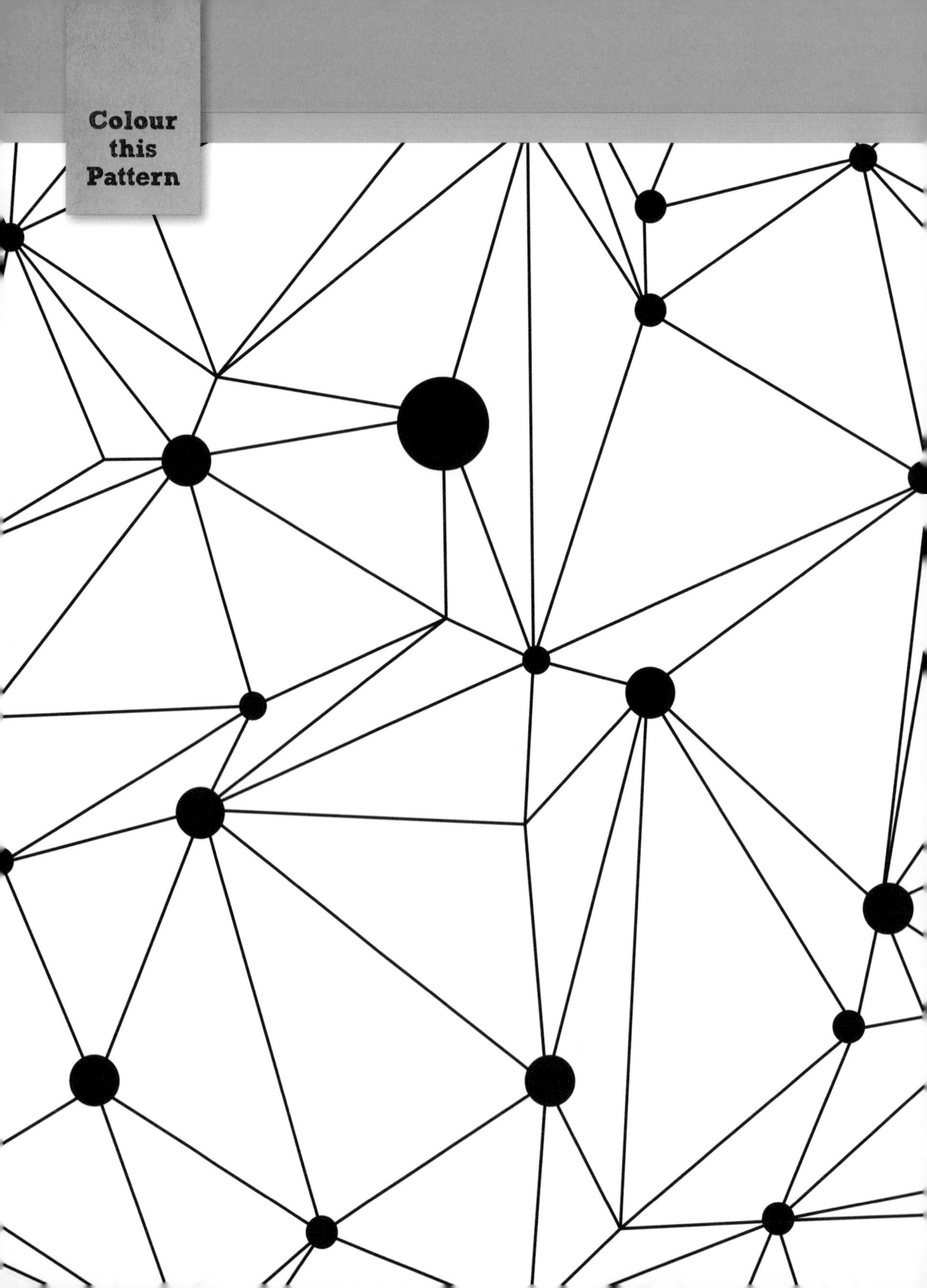
Colour
this
Pattern

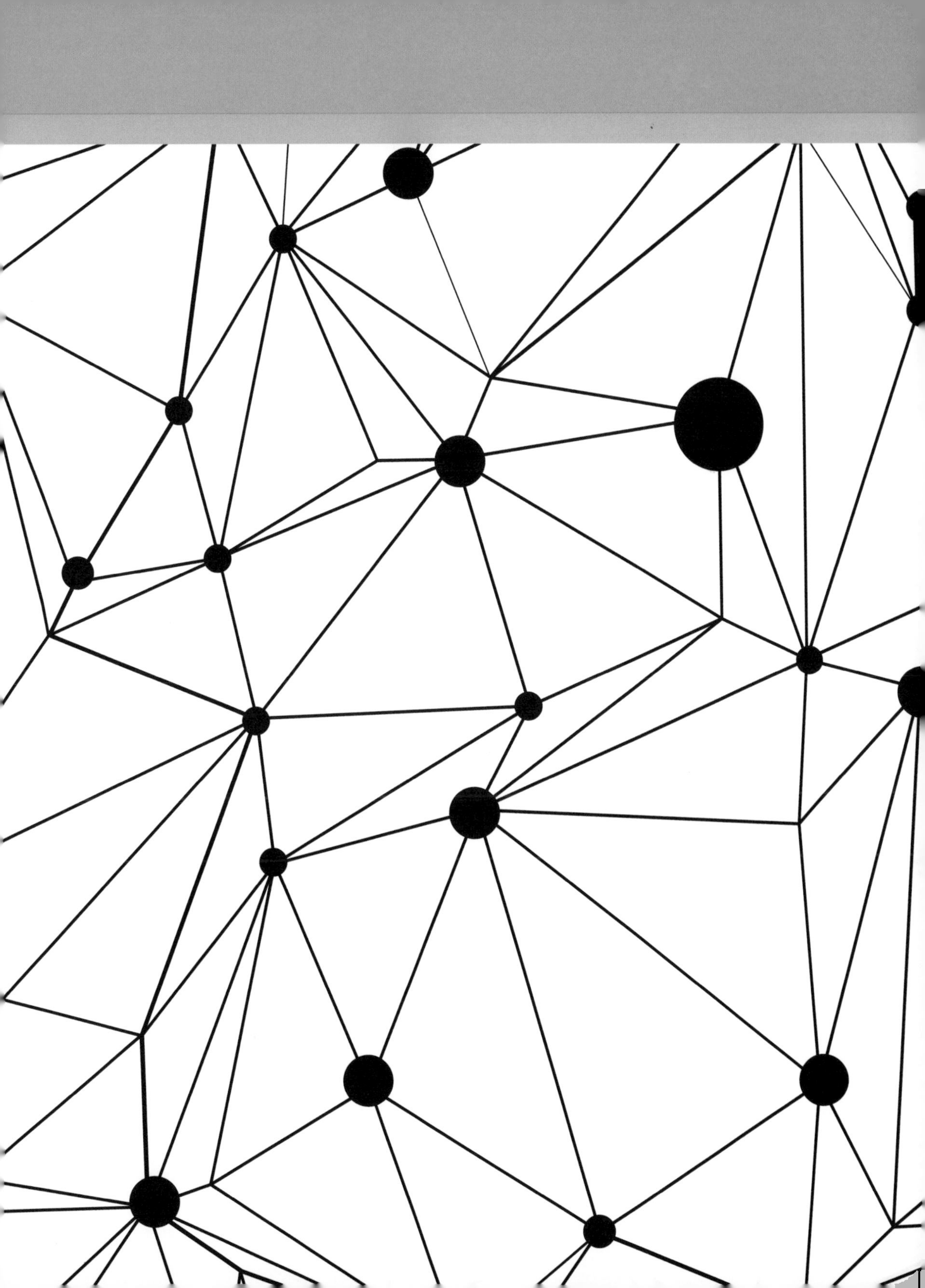

41 Musical Instruments

Our colour goes up to 11.

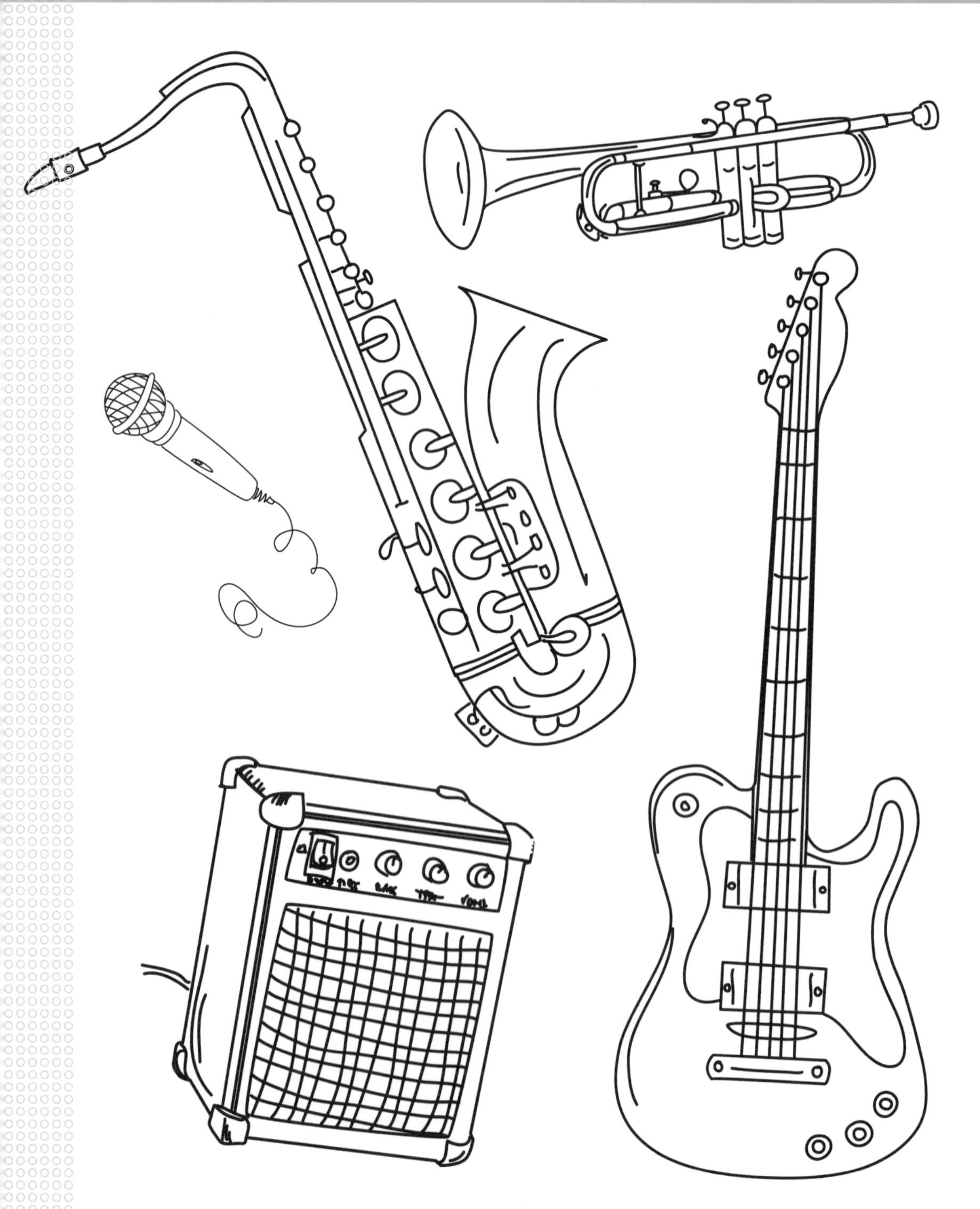

Colour
this
Pattern

42 Knick-knacks

Quaint and quirky.

Colour
this
Pattern

43 Fans

Keeping cool.

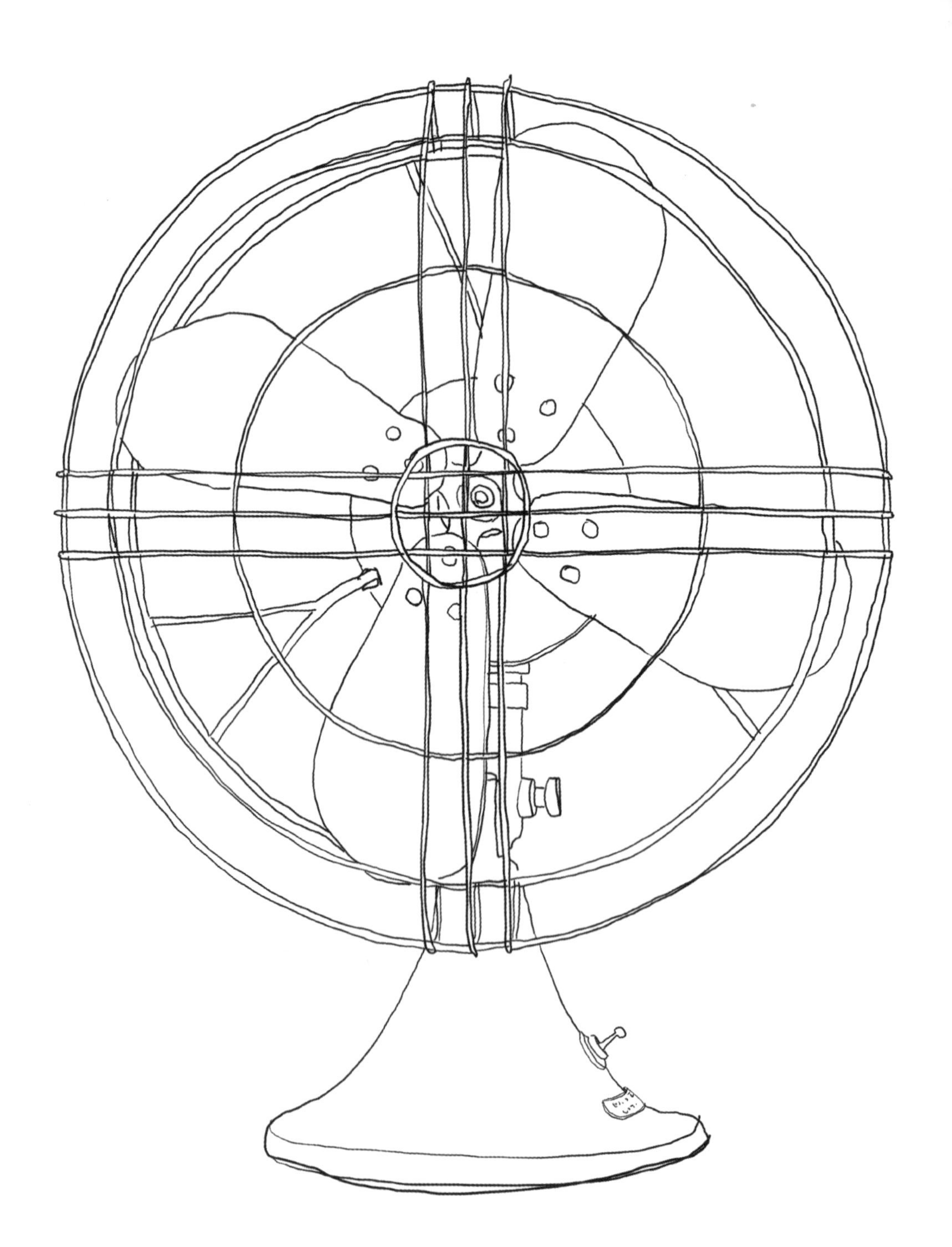

Colour
this
Pattern

44 Vintage Toys

Colour yourself a child again.

NYC
TAXI

Colour this Pattern

45 Vintage Telephones

Ring! Ring! It's colour calling.

1
2
3
4
5
6
7
8
9
0

Colour
this
Pattern

46 Buildings

I can see my house from here! (It's the neon one.)

Colour this Pattern

47 Headphones

Can't hear you. Colouring.

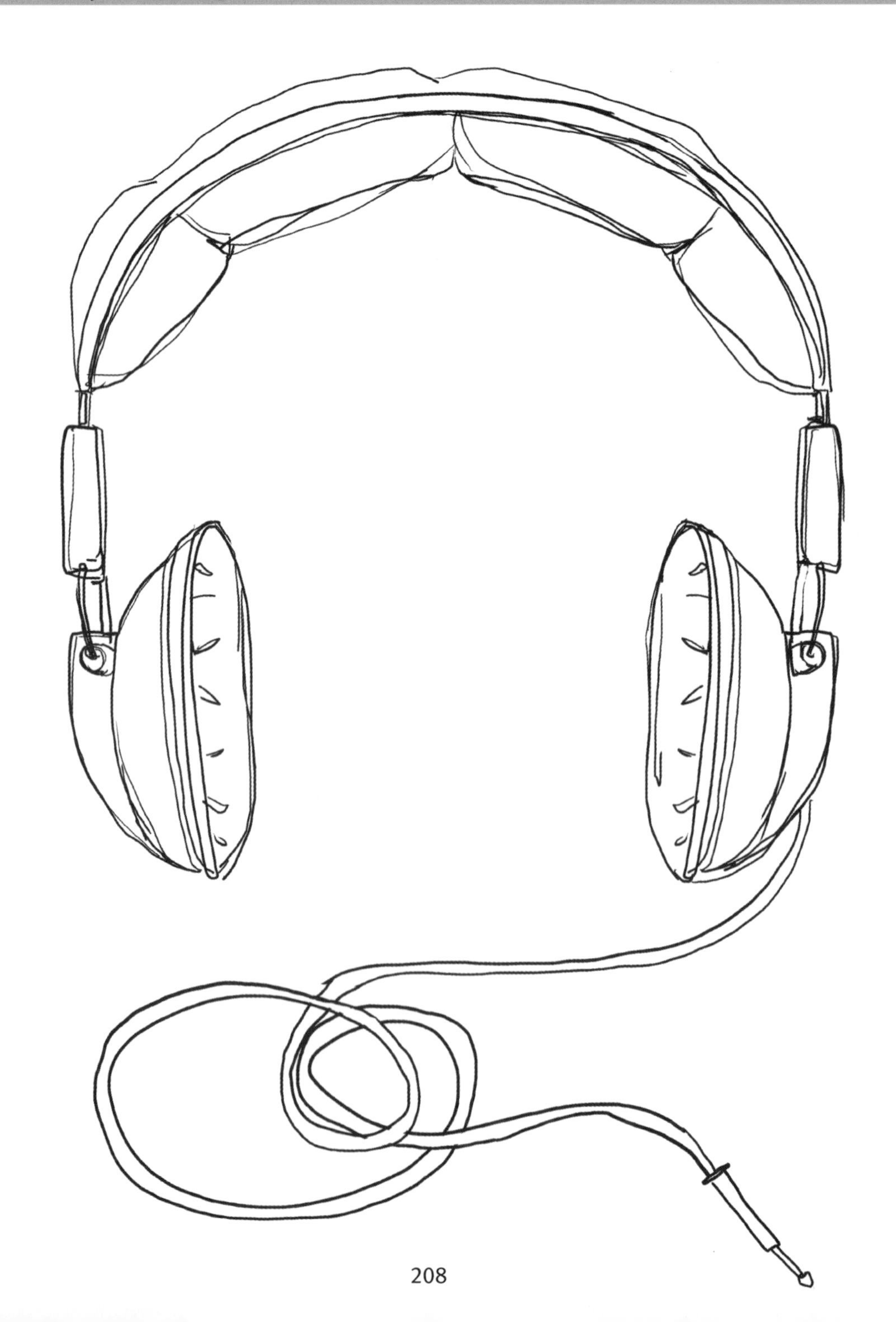

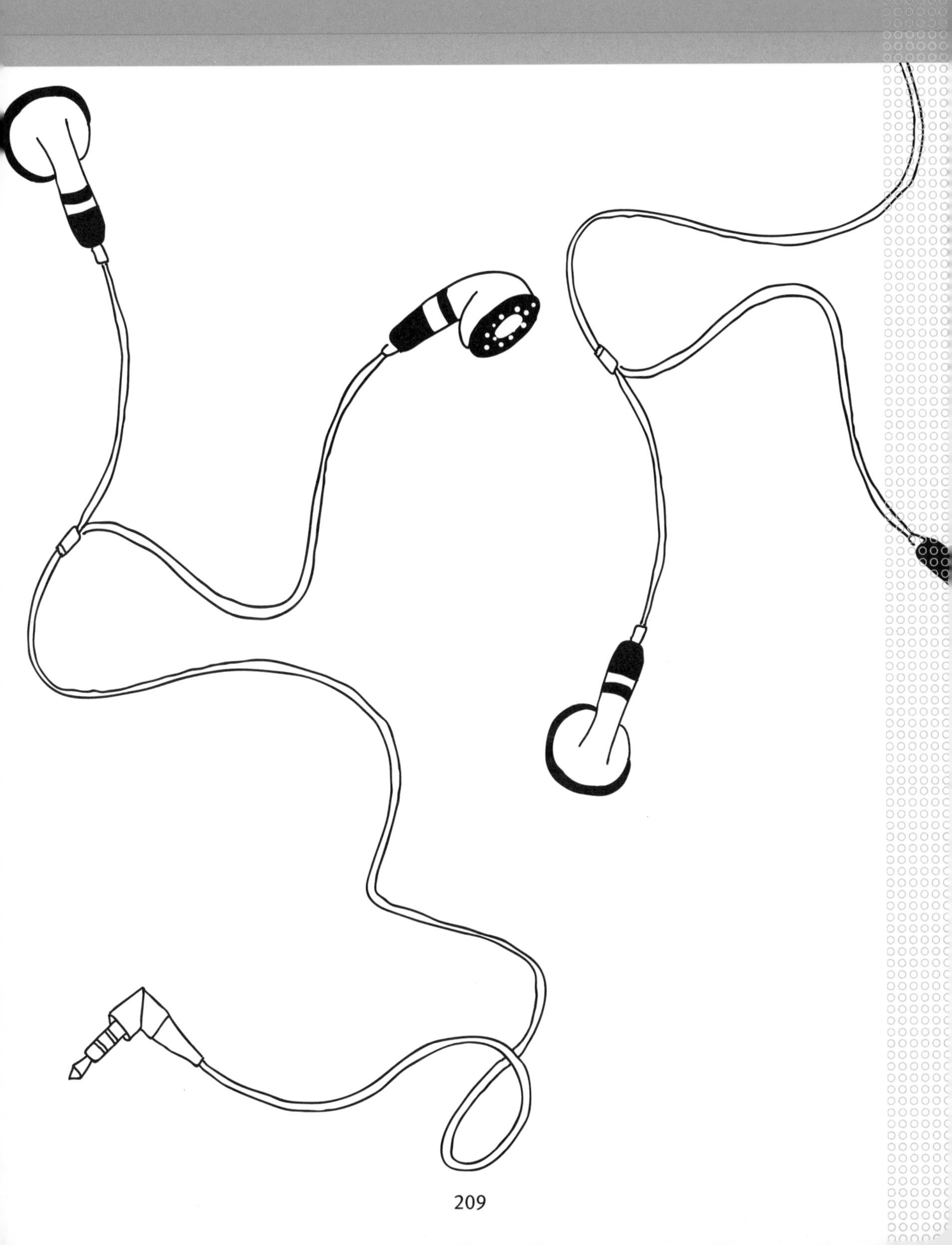

Colour
this
Pattern

48 Furniture

Sit down. Relax. Stay a while.

Colour
this
Pattern

49 Keys

The key to relaxation? Open the door to colour.

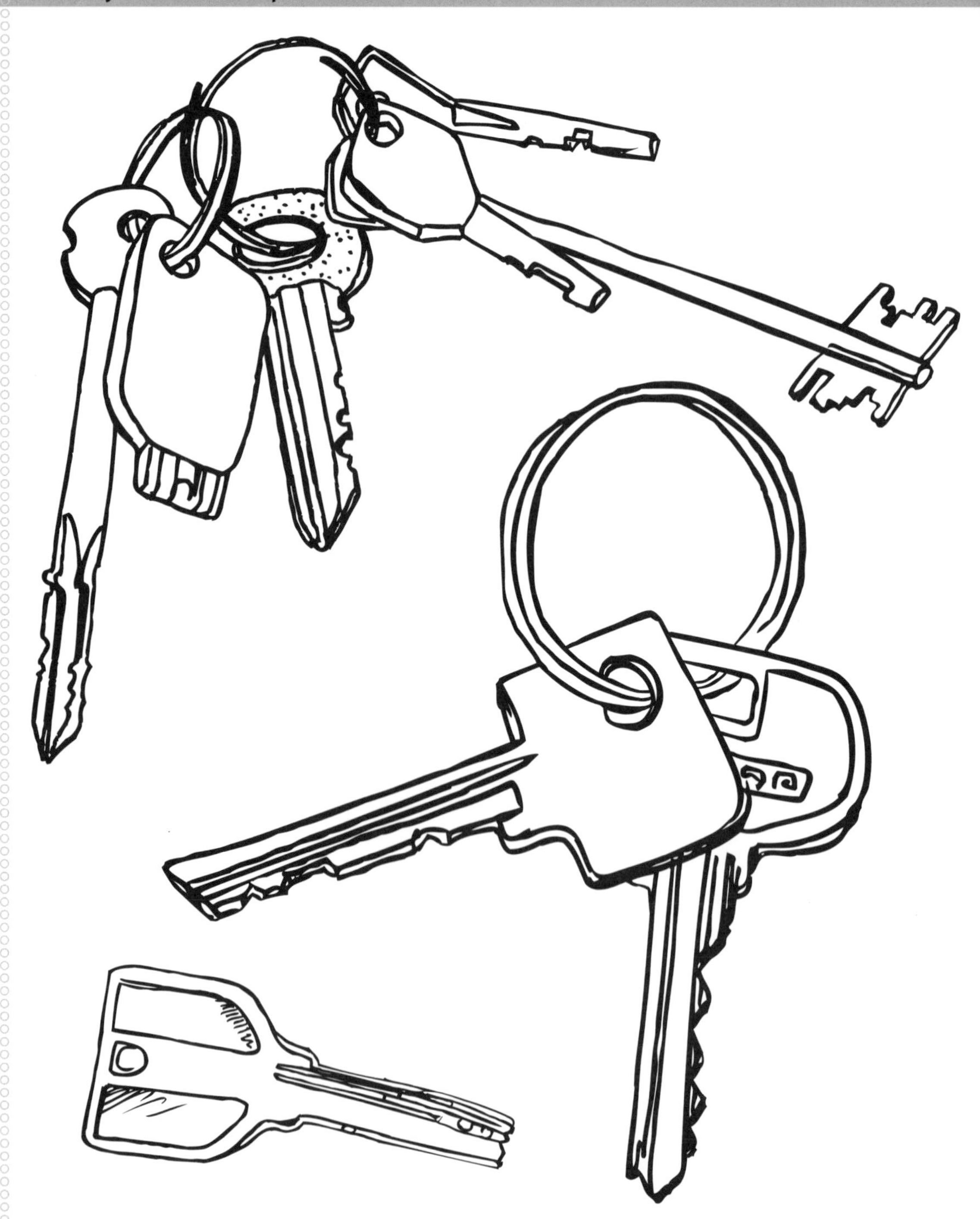

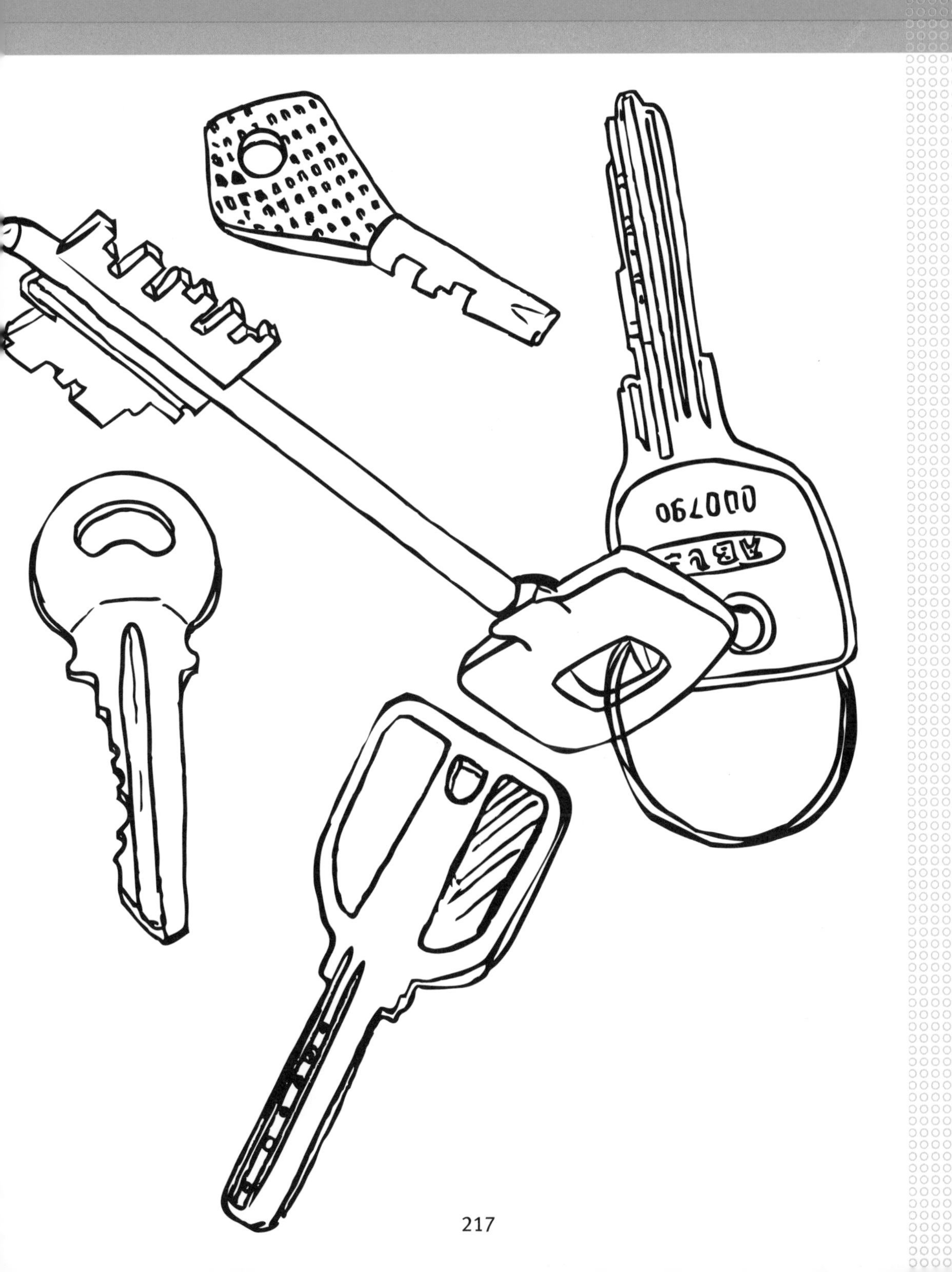

Colour
this
Pattern
75

75

50 Vehicles

Day-glo school bus? What about a double-decker!

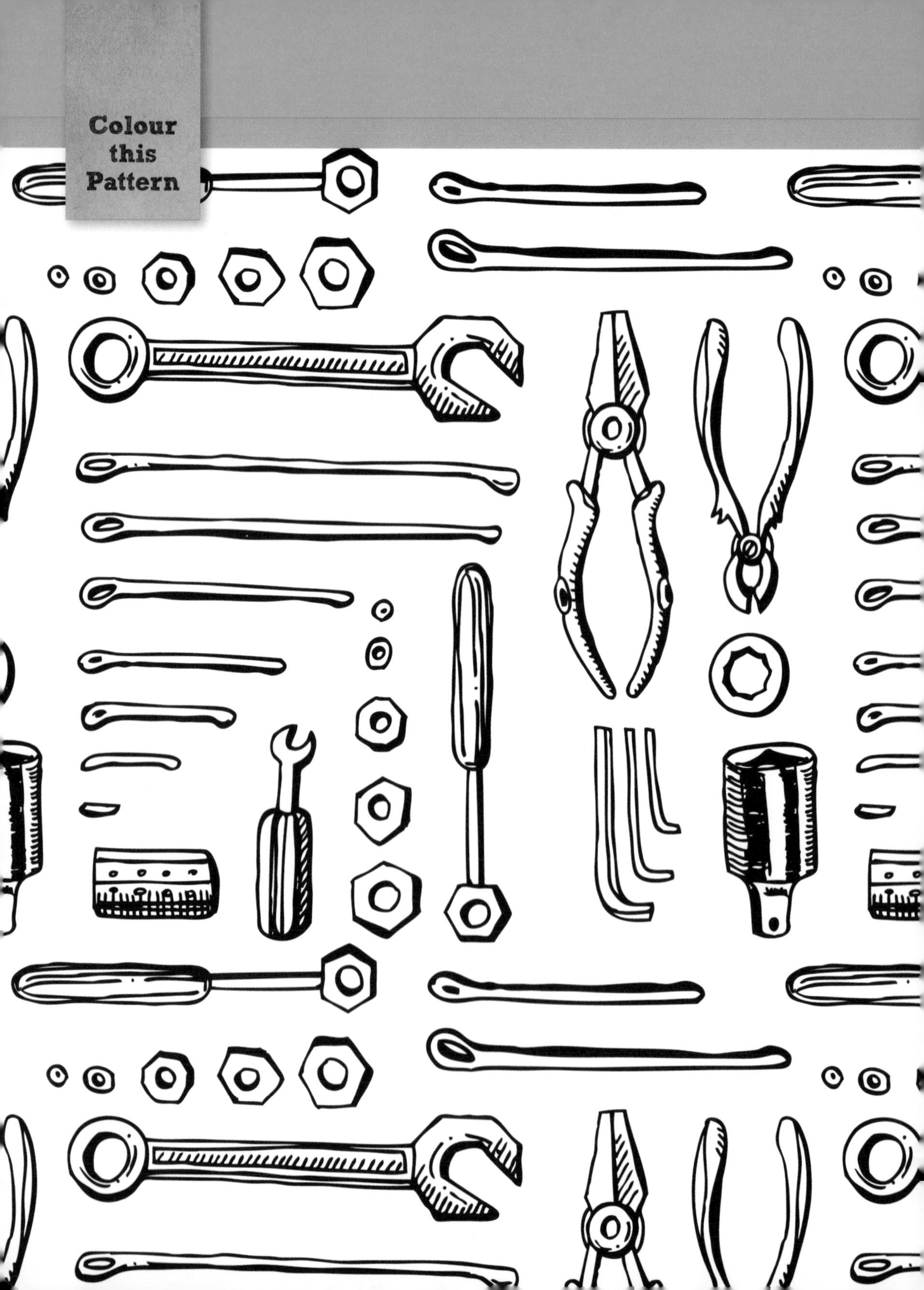
Colour
this
Pattern

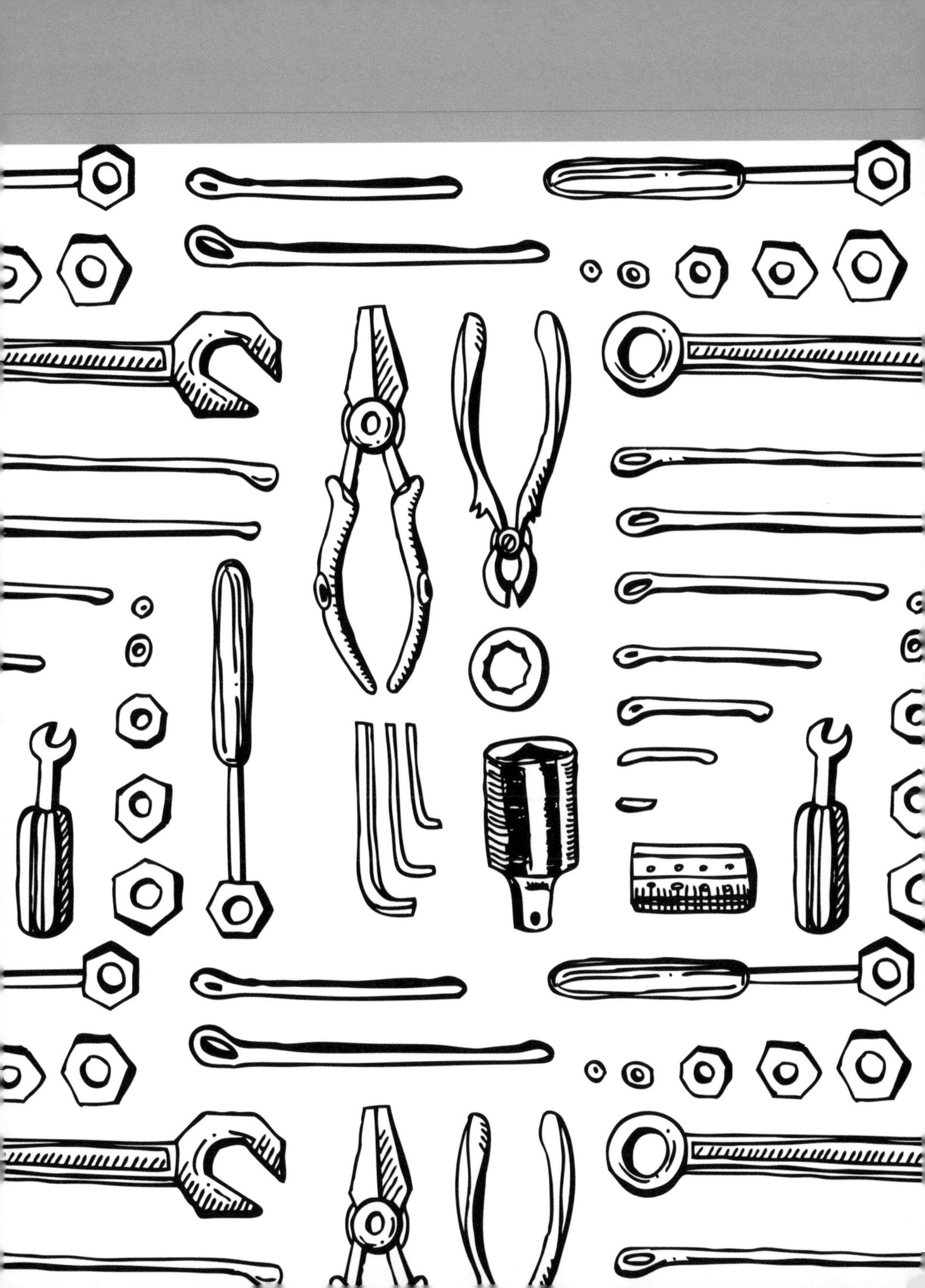

Infinite Things to Colour

You've just been initiated into a world of colour – a world where hues of vibrancy glow in places you would never expect – the side of a double-decker bus, a typewriter, sunglasses... and places you might, like a shiny scarab beetle, robust autumn leaves and packed suitcases, but perhaps in colours not necessarily expected. (Neon trees? Why not?) There might be fifty things to colour here, but there are countless more beyond. You're armed with inspiration. Colour your world bold and bright.